6 HSPT Math Practice Tests

Extra Practice to Achieve a Crack Score

By

Elise Baniam & Michael Smith

6 HSPT Math Practice Tests

Published in the United State of America By

The Math Notion

Email: info@mathnotion.com

Web: www.mathnotion.com

ISBN: 978-1-63620-184-9

About the Author

Elise Baniam has been a math instructor for over a decade now. She graduated in Mathematics. Since 2006, Elise has devoted his time to both teaching and developing exceptional math learning materials. As a math instructor and test prep expert, Elise has worked with thousands of students. She has used the feedback of her students to develop a unique study program that can be used by students to drastically improve their math score fast and effectively.

- **SAT Math Workbook**
- **ACT Math Workbook**
- **GRE Math Workbook**
- **HSPT Math Workbook**
- **Common Core Math Workbook**
- **many Math Education Workbooks**
- **and some Mathematics books …**

As an experienced Math teacher, Mrs. Baniam employs a variety of formats to help students achieve their goals: she teaches students in large groups, and she provides training materials and textbooks through her website and through Amazon.

You can contact Elise via email at:

Elise@mathnotion.com

6 Practice Tests to Help Achieve an Excellent HSPT Math Score!

Practice makes perfect, and the best way to exercise your HSPT test-taking skills is with simulated tests. Our experts selected these targeted questions to help you study more realistically and use your review time wisely to reach your best score. These math questions are the same as the ones you will find on the HSPT test, so you will know what to expect and avoid surprises on test day.

6 HSPT Math Practice Tests provide six full-length opportunities to evaluate whether you have the skills to ace the test's higher-level math questions.

This book emphasizes that any difficult math question focuses on building a solid understanding of basic mathematical concepts. Inside the practice math book, you will find realistic HSPT math questions and detailed explanations to help you master your math sections of the HSPT. You will discover everything you need to ace the test, including:

- Aligned to the latest HSPT test.
- **Fully explained answers to all questions.**
- Practice questions that help you increase speed and accuracy.
- Learn fundamental approaches for achieving content mastery.
- Diagnose and learn from your mistakes with in-depth answer explanations.

With the HSPT math prep, the lots of test takers who would like an intensive drill with multiple math questions, get a quick but full review of everything on their exam. Anyone planning to take the HSPT exam should take advantage of math practice tests. Purchase it today to receive access to HSPT math practice questions.

WWW.MATHNOTION.COM

… So Much More Online!

✓ FREE Math Lessons

✓ More Math Learning Books!

✓ Mathematics Worksheets

✓ Online Math Tutors

For a PDF Version of This Book

Please Visit www.mathnotion.com

Contents

HSPT Test Review

HSPT Test Mathematics Formula Sheet

Area of a:

Parallelogram	$A = bh$
Trapezoid	$A = \dfrac{1}{2}h(b_1 + b_2)$

Surface Area and Volume of a:

Rectangular/Right Prism	$SA = ph + 2B$	$V = Bh$
Cylinder	$SA = 2\pi rh + 2\pi r^2$	$V = \pi r^2 h$
Pyramid	$SA = \dfrac{1}{2}ps + B$	$V = \dfrac{1}{3}Bh$
Cone	$SA = \pi rs + \pi r^2$	$V = \dfrac{1}{3}\pi r^2 h$
Sphere	$SA = 4\pi r^2$	$V = \dfrac{4}{3}\pi r^3$

(p = perimeter of base B; $\pi = 3.14$)

Algebra

Slope of a line	$m = \dfrac{y_2 - y_1}{x_2 - x_1}$
Slope-intercept form of the equation of a line	$y = mx + b$
Point-slope form of the Equation of a line	$y - y_1 = m(x - x_1)$
Standard form of a Quadratic equation	$y = ax^2 + bx + c$
Quadratic formula	$x = \dfrac{-b \pm \sqrt{b^2 - 4ac}}{2a}$
Pythagorean theorem	$a^2 + b^2 = c^2$
Simple interest	$I = prt$

(I = interest, p = principal, r = rate, t = time)

HSPT Practice Test 1

Mathematics

Total Number of Questions: 64 Questions

Total time: 45 Minutes

You may NOT use a calculator for this test.

Administered *Month Year*

1) How many odd integers are between $\frac{-46}{5}$ and $\frac{57}{7}$?

    A. 6

    B. 7

    C. 9

    D. 10

2) Which expression correctly represents the distance between the two points shown on the number line?

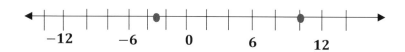

    A. $-3 - 10$

    B. $|-3 + 10|$

    C. $-3 + 10$

    D. $|3 + 10|$

3) In the triangle ABC, if angle B and angle C both equal 60°, then what is the length of side BC?

    A. 6 cm

    B. 3 cm

    C. 15 cm

    D. 9 cm

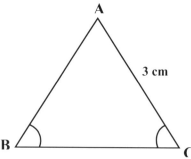

4) Which of the following represents the sum of the factors of 12?

    A. 28

    B. 30

    C. 18

    D. 26

5) Alice read $\frac{1}{4}$ of her book on Saturday and $\frac{2}{7}$ of her book on Sunday. What fraction of her book remains to be read?

    A. $\frac{13}{14}$

    B. $\frac{13}{28}$

    C. $\frac{15}{28}$

    D. $\frac{11}{14}$

6) Complete the following pattern. 27,000; 900; _____;1; _____; _____.

    A. 40; 0.044; 0.0011

    B. 30; 0.033; 0.0011

    C. 300; 0.03; 0.0033

    D. 90; 0.09; 0.0099

7) Find the greatest common factor of 14, 35, and 30.

    A. 1

    B. 3

    C. 15

    D. 10

8) Which equation can be equal "9 more than the ratio of a number to 6 is equal to

8 less than the number"?

A. $9x - 6 = 8 - x$

B. $9 + \frac{x}{6} = x - 8$

C. $\frac{9}{8}x - 6 = 6x$

D. $9 + 6x = 8 - x$

9) Arrange the following fractions in order from least to greatest.

$$\frac{5}{9}, \frac{2}{5}, \frac{1}{8}, \frac{25}{28}, \frac{12}{17}$$

A. $\frac{1}{8}, \frac{2}{5}, \frac{5}{9}, \frac{12}{17}, \frac{25}{28}$

B. $\frac{2}{5}, \frac{5}{9}, \frac{1}{8}, \frac{12}{17}, \frac{25}{28}$

C. $\frac{25}{28}, \frac{12}{17}, \frac{2}{5}, \frac{5}{9}, \frac{1}{8}$

D. $\frac{12}{17}, \frac{25}{28}, \frac{1}{8}, \frac{5}{9}, \frac{2}{5}$

10) Elena earn $6.5 an hour and worked 36 hours. Her brother earns $9.75 an hour.

How many hours would her brother need to work to equal Elena's earnings

over 40 hours?

A. 19.5

B. 24

C. 30

D. 32

11) In a library, 20% of the books are fiction and the rest are non-fiction. Given that there are 1,500 more non-fiction books than fiction books, what is the total number of books in the library?

    A. 3,000

    B. 4,500

    C. 2,500

    D. 1,600

12) A map has the scale of 6 cm to 1 km. What is the actual area of a lake on ground which is represented as an area of 90 cm^2 on the map?

    A. 2.4 km^2

    B. 2.5 km^2

    C. 18 cm^2

    D. 2.8 cm^2

13) $15.15 \div 0.3 =$

    A. 5.05

    B. 50.50

    C. 50.05

    D. 5.005

14) What is the circumference of a circle with a radius of 9 inches?

   A. $81\,\pi$

   B. $18\,\pi$

   C. $9\,\pi$

   D. $36\,\pi$

15) Alfred needs to calculate his monthly water bill. His family used 31,500 gallons at a rate of $0.86 per hundred gallons. Also, there is a monthly fee of $5.30 on each period. What is his total bill?

   A. $3,325.20

   B. $367.30

   C. $276.2

   D. $27.62

16) Simplify $\dfrac{(3x^4 - 6x^3)}{(x^3 - 2x^2)} = ?$

   A. $3x$

   B. $x - 2$

   C. $6x$

   D. $2x(x - 1)$

17) Which of the following expressions is undefined in the set of real numbers?

   A. $\sqrt[2]{121}$

   B. $\sqrt[3]{-64}$

   C. $\sqrt{-25}$

   D. $\sqrt[4]{81}$

18) If $f(x) = 6x^2$, and 4f(3a) = 864 then what could be the value of a?

   A. -2

   B. -4

   C. 4

   D. 2

19) Speed of a train is 140 miles per hour for 3 hours and 25 minutes. How many miles did the train travel?

   A. 455

   B. 285

   C. 355

   D. 265

20) Solve $5x - 8 \le 12x + 6$

   A. $x \le -2$

   B. $x \ge -2$

   C. $x \le 2$

   D. $x \ge 2$

21) What is the value of 2^8?

    A. $(2 + 2)^8$

    B. 4^4

    C. $2(2^4)$

    D. $2^4 + 2^4$

22) Shane Williams puts $4,200 into a saving bank account that pays simple interest of 3.8%. How much interest will she earn after 5 years?

    A. $2,780

    B. $ 1,198

    C. $798

    D. $189

23) Three angles join to form a straight angle. One angle measure 61°. Other angle measures 42°. What is the measure of third angle?

    A. 17°

    B. 27°

    C. 103°

    D. 77°

24) Evaluate $\dfrac{15x^7y^4z^{-4}}{6\,x^3y^8z^2}$.

    A. $\dfrac{5x^4y^4}{2\,z^6}$

    B. $\dfrac{5x^3z^2}{2\,y^2}$

    C. $\dfrac{5x^4}{2\,y^4z^6}$

    D. $\dfrac{5y^4}{2\,x^4z^6}$

25) Find the equation for line passing through $(1,-2)$ and $(4,3)$.

    A. $-5x - 3y = 11$

    B. $3y - 5x = -29$

    C. $-5x + 3y = 19$

    D. $3y + 5x = -21$

26) If $x = -3$ and $y = 5$, calculate the value of $\dfrac{x^2+12}{y-2}$.

    A. $\dfrac{1}{7}$

    B. -7

    C. 7

    D. 5

27) The table shows the parking rates for the outside terminal area at an airport.

Ethan parked at the lot for $4\frac{1}{2}$ hours. How much did he owe?

A. $6.95

B. $7.55

C. $7.95

D. $6.55

3 hours	$4.2
Each 30 minutes after 3 hours	$1.25
24-hours Discount rate	$50

28) What is the value of x in term of c and d $\frac{c-d}{dx} = \frac{3}{5}$? (c and d>0)

A. $\frac{5}{3}(\frac{c}{d} - 1)$

B. $\frac{5}{3}(1 - \frac{c}{d})$

C. $\frac{3}{5}\left(\frac{c}{d} - 1\right)$

D. $\frac{3}{5}(1 - \frac{c}{d})$

29) Factor the equation $4x^4 - x^2$.

A. $2x^2(2x + 1)$

B. $x^2(2x + 1)(x - 2)$

C. $x^2(2x - 1)(x + 2)$

D. $x^2(2x - 1)(2x + 1)$

30) Which of the following are the solutions to the equation $x^2 - 16x + 63 = 0$?

   A. $-9, 3$

   B. $9, 7$

   C. $-3, -9$

   D. $9, -7$

31) Which of the following equations best represents the line in the graph below?

   A. $y = \frac{1}{4}x + 1$

   B. $y = x + 4$

   C. $y = \frac{1}{4}x - 1$

   D. $y = 4x + 1$

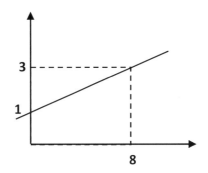

32) If $-4x + 5y = -4$ and $3x - 2y = 3$, what is the value of x?

   A. 3

   B. 0

   C. -3

   D. 1

33) lengths of Two sides of a triangle are 7 and 4. Which of the following could

   Not be the measure of third side?

   A. 5

   B. 2

   C. 12

   D. 14

34) The following data set is given: 121, 149, 136, 174, 167, 129

Adding which number to the set will increase its mean?

A. 142

B. 145

C. 141

D. 151

35) An award for best education improvement is awarded annually to a winning

US state, and the winners from 2002 to 2011 are given in the table below. Find

the mode of this set of states.

Year	2002	2003	2004	2005	2006	2007	2008	2009	2010	2011
State	New Jersey	Ohio	Oregon	New York	Oregon	California	Ohio	Oregon	Ohio	New Jersey

A. New York and Oregon

B. California and New Jersey

C. Ohio and Oregon

D. Oregon and California

36) How long is a distance of 9 km if measured on a map with a scale of

1:60,000?

A. 18

B. 15

C. 9

D. 5

37) What is the area of a square, if its side measures $\sqrt{11}$ m?

A. $\sqrt{11}$

B. $2\sqrt{11}$

C. $3\sqrt{11}$

D. 11

38) What is the answer of the following equation $3x^3y^2 (2x^2y^2)^5 =$?

A. $64x^{13}y^{12}$

B. $96x^{13}y^{12}$

C. $96x^{12}y^{13}$

D. $64x^{12}y^{13}$

39) The circle graph below shows the type of pizza that people prefer for lunch. If 180 people were surveyed, how many people preferred Meat lover's?

A. 26

B. 28

C. 27

D. 24

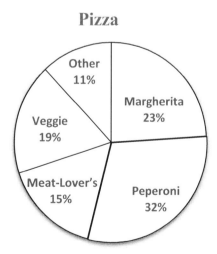

Pizza

40) Rosie is x years old. She is 6 years older than her twin brothers Milan and

Marcel. What is the mean age of the three children?

A. $x + 4$

B. $x - 9$

C. $x + 9$

D. $x - 4$

41) a is inversely proportional to $(3b - 8)$. If a = 12 and b = 6, express a in terms

of b.

A. $a = 3b - 14$

B. $a = 120(3b - 8)$

C. $a = \frac{120}{3b-8}$

D. $a = \frac{3b-8}{120}$

42) A baseball has a volume of 972π. What is the length of the diameter?

A. 27

B. 18

C. 9

D. 15

43) 168 is What percent of 120?

A. 140 %

B. 40 %

C. 60 %

D. 160 %

44) A phone manufacturer makes 15,000 phone a year. The company randomly selects 300 of the phones to sample for inspection. The company discovers that there are 4 faulty phones in the sample. Based on the sample, how many of the 15,000 total phones are likely to be faulty?

A. 400

B. 30

C. 150

D. 200

45) Emma and Mia buy a total of 25 books. Emma bought 3 more books than Mia did. How many books did Emma buy?

A. 13

B. 14

C. 16

D. 7

46) A bag contains 3 white balls, 7 red balls and 4 black balls. A ball is picked from the bag at random. Find the probability of picking a red ball?

A. 1.20

B. 0.20

C. 0.05

D. 0.50

47) The radius of the following cylinder is 3 inches and its height are 7 inches.

What is the surface area of the cylinder in square inches? (π=3.14)

A. 188.4

B. 376.8

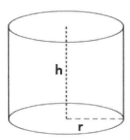

h

C. 9.42

D. 37.68

r

48) Find the length of the unknown side.

A. 28 ft

B. 35 ft

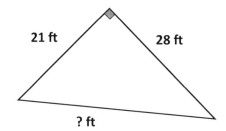

21 ft   28 ft

C. 30 ft

D. 48 ft

? ft

49) The line n has a slope of $\frac{a}{b}$, where c and d are integers. What is the slope of a

line that is perpendicular to line n?

A. $\frac{a}{b}$

B. $-\frac{a}{b}$

C. $\frac{b}{a}$

D. $-\frac{b}{a}$

50) For what value(s) of x is the following equation true: $2x^2 - 16x + 32 = 0$?

   A. $4, 8$

   B. $+4$

   C. -4

   D. ± 4

51) Solve the linear inequality: $-\dfrac{(3x-9)}{5} + 7 \geq 10$

   A. $x \leq -2$

   B. $x > -2$

   C. $x \geq -2$

   D. $x < -2$

52) Evaluate: $\dfrac{(x^2+7x+12)}{(2x^2-4x+2)} \div \dfrac{(x^2-x-20)}{(x^2-6x+5)} = ?$

   A. $\dfrac{x+3}{2x+2}$

   B. $\dfrac{2(x-2)}{x-3}$

   C. $\dfrac{x+3}{2x-2}$

   D. $\dfrac{2x+2}{x-3}$

53) In a store, 22% of customers are female. If the total number of customers is 800, then how many male customers are dealing with the store?

    A. 286

    B. 864

    C. 624

    D. 426

54) If 72.3 kg is divided into two parts, in a ratio of 7:4, how many kg is the smaller share?

    A. 2.96 kg

    B. 26.29 kg

    C. 2.62 kg

    D. 29.26 kg

55) Express as a single fraction in its simplest form: $\dfrac{3}{(x-1)} - \dfrac{4}{(2x+3)} = ?$

    A. $\dfrac{2x+13}{(x-1)(2x+3)}$

    B. $\dfrac{2x-13}{(x-1)(3x+2)}$

    C. $\dfrac{2x+13}{2x+3}$

    D. $\dfrac{-2}{2x-13}$

56) Ryan is x years old, and her sister Mitzi is $(7x - 16)$ years old. Given that Mitzi is triple as old as Ryan, what is Mitzi's age?

   A. 8

   B. 10

   C. 12

   D. 16

57) The set of possible values of p is $\{4, 8, 12\}$. What is the set of possible values of h if $4h = 3p + 4$?

   A. {4,10,12}

   B. {7,10,12}

   C. $\{4, 7, 10\}$

   D. {7,12,14}

58) In the infinitely repeating decimal below, 7 is the second digit in the repeating pattern. What is the 440st digit? $\frac{1}{13} = \overline{0.076923}$

   A. 7

   B. 6

   C. 0

   D. 3

59) $\frac{1}{6} = (?)\frac{2}{9}$

    A. 25%

    B. 82%

    C. 56%

    D. 75%

60) Consider the following series: 2, 4, 6, 8, 12, 18. What number should come next?

    A. 29

    B. 31

    C. 26

    D. 28

61) Evaluate: $(2y - 3x)(4x - y)$?

    A. $-2x^2 - 11xy + 12y^2$

    B. $2x^2 - 11xy + 12y^2$

    C. $-12x^2 + 11xy - 2y^2$

    D. $12x^2 - 11xy + 2y^2$

62) Solve for y: $2.75 - 0.4y = -0.37$

    A. 6.55

    B. 4.55

    C. 7.8

    D. 8.5

63) Steven wants to make a platform that is 6 feet wide and 12 feet long. If he uses boards that measure 18 inches wide by 6 feet long, how many boards will he need to complete the job?

    A. 24

    B. 8

    C. 16

    D. 4

64) A cube has a side length of 120 cm, what is its volume in cubic meters?

    $(100\ cm = 1\ m)$

    A. 14.28

    B. 1.288

    C. 1.44

    D. 1.728

"End of HSPT Practice Test 1."

HSPT Practice Test 2

Mathematics

Total Number of Questions: 64 Questions

Total time: 45 Minutes

You may NOT use a calculator for this test.

Administered *Month Year*

1) What is the sum of the smallest prime number and six times the largest negative even integer?

   A. -6

   B. 4

   C. -10

   D. -8

2) Sam's incomes and expenditures for the first season of the last year are given in the table below. In which month were her savings the highest?

   A. February

   B. March

   C. January

   D. All months were the same

Month	Income	Cost
January	$2,780	$1,002
February	$2,895	$975
March	$2,990	$1,012

3) What is the number a, if the result of adding a to 38 is the same as subtracting $5a$ from 272?

   A. -49

   B. 57

   C. 127

   D. 39

4) Solve these fractions and reduce to its simplest terms: $7\frac{5}{32} - 4\frac{1}{4} + 3\frac{3}{8} =$

   A. $6\frac{9}{32}$

   B. $-6\frac{5}{32}$

   C. $\frac{5}{8}$

   D. $6\frac{3}{4}$

5) Calculate, $5^2 + 5 + 5^0 = ?$

   A. 5^2

   B. 35

   C. 31

   D. 75

6) Which decimal is equivalent to $\frac{133}{190}$?

   A. 0.107

   B. 1.07

   C. 0.07

   D. 0.7

7) The price of a shirt increased from \$40 to \$42.40. What is the percentage increase in the price?

   A. 6%

   B. 0.6%

   C. 0.94%

   D. 1.6%

8) Find the solution set of the following equation: $|3x - 6| = 9$

    A. $\{5, -1\}$

    B. $\{1, -5\}$

    C. $\{1\}$

    D. $\{-5, -1\}$

9) What is the solution to the pair of equations below? $\begin{cases} x - 4y = 6 \\ 3x + y = 5 \end{cases}$

    A. $x = 1$ and $y = -2$

    B. $x = -1$ and $y = 2$

    C. $x = 2$ and $y = -1$

    D. $x = 2$ and $y = -2$

10) The train each 20 minutes passes an average 3 stations. At this rate, how many stations will it pass in four hours.

    A. 24

    B. 36

    C. 18

    D. 72

11) If Sofia buy a shirt marked down 12 percent from its $170 while Natalia buys

the same shirt mark down only 10 percent, how much more does Natalia pay

for the shirt?

A. $0.34

B. $1.70

C. $17

D. $3.40

12) Find the circumference of the circle in terms of π.

A. 14.5π in.

B. 29π in.

C. 58 π in.

D. 116π in.

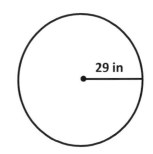

29 in

13) Find the volume of rectangular prism below?

A. 980 in^3

B. 1,090 in^3

C. 2,990 in^3

D. 5,880 in^3

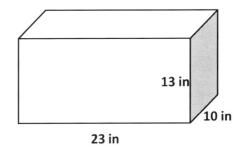

13 in

10 in

23 in

14) What is $\sqrt[3]{3^{-9}}$ in simplest form?

A. $\dfrac{1}{2,187}$

B. $\dfrac{1}{729}$

C. $\dfrac{1}{9}$

D. $\dfrac{1}{27}$

15) Which statement correctly describes the value of N in the equation below?

$5(9N - 11) = 9(5N - 13)$?

A. N has no correct solutions.

B. N has infinitely many correct solutions.

C. N=1 is one solution.

D. N=0 is one solution.

16) What is the maximum amount of grain, the silo can hold, in cubic feet?

A. $480\pi\ m^3$

B. $148\pi\ m^3$

C. $408\pi\ m^3$

D. $1,630\pi\ m^3$

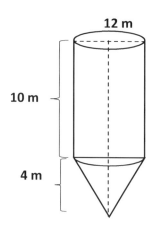

17) What is 7.59×10^{-3} in standard form?

    A. –75,900

    B. –0.00759

    C. $\dfrac{1}{75,900}$

    D. 0.00759

18) What is the value of x in the triangle?

    A. 44°

    B. 134°

    C. 46°

    D. 131°

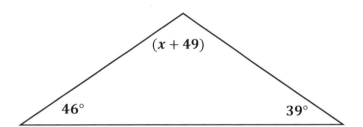

19) Find the length of the unknown side.

    A. 28 ft

    B. 24 ft

    C. 22 ft

    D. 26 ft

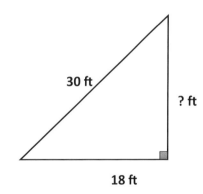

20) A store sells all of its products at a price 15% greater than the price the store paid for the product. How much does the store sell a product if the store paid $160 for it?

A. $248

B. $124

C. $184

D. $24

21) What is the area of shaded region?

A. 68

B. 92

C. 24

D. 106

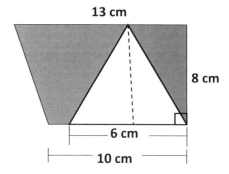

22) if $xy - 9x = 42$ and $y - 9 = 7$, then $x =$?

A. 4

B. 12

C. 7

D. 6

23) Which is the value of x in the equation $\frac{x}{5} = x - 8$?

    A. 5

    B. 13

    C. 10

    D. 8

24) What is the value of x, If $-7x + 3y = 8$ and $-6x + 5y = 2$?

    A. -8

    B. -1

    C. -6

    D. -2

25) What is the probability of Not spinning at H?

    A. $\frac{1}{2}$

    B. $\frac{1}{8}$

    C. $\frac{1}{4}$

    D. $\frac{3}{8}$

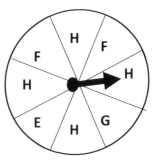

26) Ella bought 42 movies for \$4.06 per movie. Which equation shows the BEST

    estimate of the total cost?

    A. $40 \times \$4 = \$160$

    B. $40 \times \$5 = \$200$

    C. $42 \times \$4 = \$168$

    D. $42 \times \$5 = \$210$

27) A pick-up truck travels 60 mile on 9 L of gasoline when driven on a smooth road. If the cost of gasoline is $1.20/L, which is the cost of 1,400 mile of highway (smooth)?

A. $151

B. $1,255

C. $125.5

D. $252

28) A position of subway station and Grace's house shown by a grid. The station is located at $(-3, -5)$, and her house is located at $(1, -2)$. What is the distance between her house and the subway stop?

A. 4

B. 5

C. $5\sqrt{2}$

D. 3

29) For the following set of numbers find the median.

230, 98, 389, 156, 215, 188, 401.

A. 215

B. 156

C. 230

D. 188

30) What is solution to the equation $\sqrt{5x - 6} = 7$?

    A. -6

    B. -12

    C. 8

    D. 11

31) The equation $x = 3y - 9$ has a y-intercept of?

    A. 3

    B. -3

    C. $\frac{1}{3}$

    D. $-\frac{1}{3}$

32) If $2^{3x} = 64$, then $x = ?$

    A. 8

    B. 1

    C. 2

    D. 6

33) Which is the smallest positive integer which is divisible by both 32 and 48.

    A. 12

    B. 48

    C. 96

    D. 120

34) A cube has total surface area of 150 cm^2. what is the volume of the cube in cm^3?

A. 5

B. 125

C. 25

D. 75

35) Which is the value of x^2, if $x^2 + 4x = 32$?

A. 9

B. -16

C. 49

D. 64

36) Each of 8 pitchers can contain up to $\frac{7}{8}$ L of water. If each of the pitcher is at least the one-fourth full, which of the following expressions represents the total amount of water, W, contained on all 8 pitchers?

A. $0.7 < w < 7$

B. $1.25 < w < 7$

C. $0.75 < w < 3.5$

D. $1.75 < w < 7$

37) Ages of the players on a volleyball team is given. Which is the range of their

ages? 27, 42, 19, 51, 25, 50, 22, 37, 30, 16, 46, 29

   A. 28

   B. 16

   C. 35

   D. 51

38) Find the area of the circle to the nearest tenth. Use 3.14 for π.

   A. 379.9

   B. 549.7

   C. 68.0

   D. 44

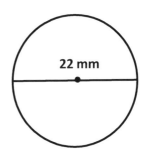

22 mm

39) What is the simplest form of the expression $\frac{3x^2-14x-5}{9(x^2-\frac{1}{9})}$?

   A. $\frac{x+5}{3(x-\frac{1}{3})}$

   B. $\frac{x-5}{3x-1}$

   C. $\frac{x+4}{3x+1}$

   D. $\frac{x-2}{x-3}$

40) What is the value of $\left(\frac{1}{2}\right)^{-5}$?

A. $\frac{1}{32}$

B. -32

C. $-\frac{1}{32}$

D. 32

41) What is the simplest form of the expression $\frac{(6x^{-4}y^2)^2}{252y^{-3}z^0}$, (using positive exponent)?

A. $\frac{y^7 z}{7x^8}$

B. $\frac{y^7}{7x^8}$

C. $\frac{7x^8}{zy^8}$

D. $\frac{x^8}{7y^7}$

42) A fruit sells for $20 per kilograms. What is the price in cent per gram?

A. 0.002

B. 0.2

C. 0.02

D. 2

43) The price of water quadruple every 5 years. If the price of water on January 1st, 2012 is \$8 per gallon, what is the equation that would be used to calculate the price(P) of water on January 1st, 2007?

A. $4P = 5$

B. $\frac{P}{8} = 4$

C. $4p = 8$

D. $8P = 4$

44) The line $3y + 4 = 18x + 7$ and $6y - 2 = x + 3$ are

A. The same line

B. Parallel

C. Perpendicular

D. Neither parallel nor perpendicular

45) A rectangular box measures $7\frac{1}{3}$ feet by $6\frac{3}{4}$ feet. It is divided into three equal parts. What is the area of one of those parts?

A. 33

B. 8.5

C. 16.5

D. 49.5

46) Find the slope of the line.

A. $\frac{1}{2}$

B. $\frac{1}{4}$

C. 4

D. $-\frac{1}{3}$

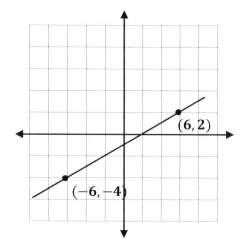

47) Amelia cuts a piece of birthday cake as shown below. What is the volume of

the piece of cake?

A. $508 \ cm^3$

B. $408 \ cm^3$

C. $480 \ cm^3$

D. $1,480 \ cm^3$

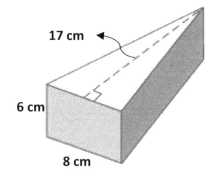

48) Let $f(x) = 3x - 6$. If $f(a) = -15$ and $f(b) = 6$, then what is $f(a + b)$?

A. 6

B. 3

C. -3

D. -6

49) Given that $10x = 4y$, find the ratio $x: y$.

    A. $5: 4$

    B. $10: 40$

    C. $5: 2$

    D. $2: 5$

50) What is the number of sides of a regular polygon whose interior angles are $162°$ each? (Remember, the sum of exterior angles of any polygon is $360°$).

    A. 4

    B. 20

    C. 16

    D. 18

51) Frank is now 7 times as old as his son Jim. three years ago, the product of their ages was 25. Find their present ages.

    A. Frank: 30 years; Jim: 9 years.

    B. Frank: 26 years; Jim: 3 years.

    C. Frank: 28 years; Jim: 4 years.

    D. Frank: 33 years; Jim: 3 years.

52) Solve the equation and choose the best answer: $\dfrac{d}{3} = \dfrac{12}{d}$

   A. -3

   B. -6

   C. 12

   D. 36

53) In a competition, three teams, FT, RT and GT, scored a total of 180 points. If FT scored 30% of this total and RT scored five times as many points as GT, what were the number of points scored by RT?

   A. 105

   B. 95

   C. 54

   D. 35

54) The sum of two consecutive integers is -19. If 3 is added to the smaller integer and 1 is subtracted from the larger integer, what is the product of the two resulting integers?

   A. 70

   B. 77

   C. 90

   D. 56

55) A sports store has a container of handballs: 12 blue, 16 red, 9 yellow, 18 white, and 5 green. If one ball is picked from the container at random, what is the probability that it will be green?

A. $\frac{1}{5}$

B. $\frac{1}{12}$

C. $\frac{1}{18}$

D. $\frac{1}{3}$

56) $4 + (7n + 9) - (8n + 3)$

A. $10 - n$

B. $10 + n$

C. $-10 - n$

D. $-10 + n$

57) Jimmy must read 134 pages for school this weekend. It took him 30 minutes to read the first 12 pages. At this rate, how much additional time will it take him to finish the reading?

A. $3\frac{1}{30}$

B. $2\frac{7}{11}$

C. $5\frac{1}{12}$

D. $6\frac{1}{32}$

58) If the line m is parallel to the side BC of ABC, what is angle n?

A. 45

B. 70

C. 20

D. 110

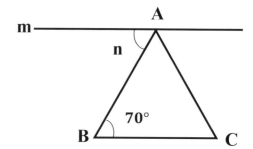

59) The cost of 1 pound of fruit is $3.10. How many pounds of food can be bought

for $15.00?

A. 0.05 pounds

B. 0.48 pounds

C. 48.0 pounds

D. 4.8 pounds

60) Given that 14 cm on a map represents 5 km on the ground, calculate the distance

in km between two points, which are 21 cm apart on the map.

A. 7.8 km

B. 7.5 km

C. 75 km

D. 78 km

61) What is the percent equivalent of 0.009?

A. 90%

B. 9%

C. 0.90%

D. 0.09%

62) When a number is subtracted from 65 and the result is divided by 4, the answer obtained is triple the original number. What is the number?

A. 5

B. 8

C. 12

D. 4

63) Tiffani's base salary last year was $45,000, not including her bonus. When she opened her HR profile, she saw that her total compensation added up to $57,000. This total included her bonus, as well as health benefits equivalent to 18% of her base salary. What percentage of Tiffani's base salary plus benefits was her bonus (Rounded to the nearest tenth)?

A. 3.3

B. 0.6

C. 7.3

D. 12.5

64) The operation is defined as $a @ b = a - 3ab$

The operation # is defined as $a\#b = a - 2b^2$

If $f(x) = -x^2 + 5$, what is the value of $\left(f(-2)@f(3)\right)\#f(1)$?

A. -42

B. -19

C. -129

D. 98

"End of HSPT Practice Test 2."

HSPT Practice Test 3

Mathematics

Total Number of Questions: 64 Questions

Total time: 45 Minutes

You may NOT use a calculator for this test.

Administered *Month Year*

1) How many odd integers are between $\dfrac{-69}{6}$ and $\dfrac{19}{5}$?

   A. 5

   B. 11

   C. 8

   D. 9

2) Which expression correctly represents the distance between the two points

   shown on the number line?

   A. $-4 - 14$

   B. $|-4 + 14|$

   C. $-4 + 14$

   D. $|4 + 14|$

3) In the triangle ABC, if angle B and angle C both equal 60°, then what is the

   length of side BC?

   A. 3 cm

   B. 6 cm

   C. 12 cm

   D. 4 cm

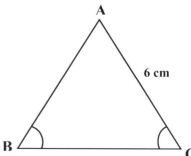

4) Which of the following represents the sum of the factors of 21?

   A. 32

   B. 29

   C. 11

   D. 23

5) Alice read $\frac{1}{5}$ of her book on Saturday and $\frac{3}{8}$ of her book on Sunday. What fraction of her book remains to be read?

   A. $\frac{19}{20}$

   B. $\frac{17}{40}$

   C. $\frac{23}{40}$

   D. $\frac{17}{20}$

6) Complete the following pattern. 16,000; 800; _____;2; _____; _____.

   A. 60; 0.03; 0.006

   B. 40; 0.1; 0.005

   C. 200; 0.02; 0.002

   D. 80; 0.08; 0.004

7) Find the greatest common factor of 20, 28, and 42.

   A. 2

   B. 1

   C. 12

   D. 20

8) Which equation can be equal "10 more than the ratio of a number to 4 is equal to 7 less than the number"?

A. $10x - 4 = 7 - x$

B. $10 + \frac{x}{4} = x - 7$

C. $\frac{10}{7}x - 4 = 4x$

D. $10 + 4x = 7 - x$

9) Arrange the following fractions in order from least to greatest.

$$\frac{3}{8}, \frac{4}{7}, \frac{1}{5}, \frac{23}{25}, \frac{14}{19}$$

A. $\frac{1}{5}, \frac{3}{8}, \frac{4}{7}, \frac{14}{19}, \frac{23}{25}$

B. $\frac{3}{8}, \frac{4}{7}, \frac{1}{5}, \frac{14}{19}, \frac{23}{25}$

C. $\frac{23}{25}, \frac{14}{19}, \frac{3}{8}, \frac{4}{7}, \frac{1}{5}$

D. $\frac{14}{19}, \frac{23}{25}, \frac{1}{5}, \frac{4}{7}, \frac{3}{8}$

10) Elena earns $7.00 an hour and worked 33 hours. Her brother earns $8.25 an hour. How many hours would her brother need to work to equal Elena's earnings over 36 hours?

A. 22.25

B. 28

C. 40

D. 30.5

11) In a library, 30% of the books are fiction and the rest are non-fiction. Given that there are 1,200 more non-fiction books than fiction books, what is the total number of books in the library?

A. 2,000

B. 2,800

C. 3,000

D. 3,500

12) A map has the scale of 5 cm to 1 km. What is the actual area of a lake on ground which is represented as an area of 85 cm^2 on the map?

A. 4.2 km^2

B. 3.4 km^2

C. 15 cm^2

D. 1.5 cm^2

13) $45.45 \div 0.9 =$

A. 50.05

B. 50.50

C. 5.05

D. 5.50

14) What is the circumference of a circle with a radius of 11 inches?

    A. 11π

    B. 22π

    C. 121π

    D. 30.25π

15) Alfred needs to calculate his monthly water bill. His family used 28,500 gallons at a rate of $0.72 per hundred gallons. Also, there is a monthly fee of $4.40 on each period. What is his total bill?

    A. $2,310.3

    B. $205.6

    C. $209.6

    D. $29.6

16) Simplify $\dfrac{(2x^4+6x^3)}{(x^3+3x^2)} = ?$

    A. $2x$

    B. $x - 3$

    C. $3x$

    D. $3x(x + 2)$

17) Which of the following expressions is undefined in the set of real numbers?

    A. $\sqrt[2]{144}$

    B. $\sqrt[3]{-27}$

    C. $\sqrt{-49}$

    D. $\sqrt[4]{254}$

18) If $f(x) = 3x^2$, and 5f(2a) = 180 then what could be the value of a?

    A. -3

    B. -6

    C. 6

    D. 3

19) Speed of a train is 160 miles per hour for 4 hours and 45 minutes. How many miles did the train travel?

    A. 712

    B. 625

    C. 725

    D. 655

20) Solve $9x - 7 \leq 15x + 11$

    A. $x \leq -3$

    B. $x \geq -3$

    C. $x \leq 3$

    D. $x \geq 3$

21) What is the value of 3^6?

    A. $(2 + 2)^8$

    B. 9^3

    C. $3(3^2)$

    D. $3^3 + 3^3$

22) Shane Williams puts $3,600 into a saving bank account that pays simple interest of 4.5%. How much interest will she earn after 2 years?

    A. $2,845

    B. $ 2,324

    C. $324

    D. $146

23) Three angles join to form a straight angle. One angle measure 72°. Other angle measures 34°. What is the measure of third angle?

    A. 18°

    B. 68°

    C. 106°

    D. 74°

24) Evaluate $\dfrac{21x^9y^2z^{-3}}{14\,x^5y^6z^3}$.

   A. $\dfrac{3x^4y^3}{2\,z^2}$

   B. $\dfrac{3x^3z^2}{2\,y^2}$

   C. $\dfrac{3x^4}{2\,y^4z^6}$

   D. $\dfrac{7y^3}{2\,x^2z^3}$

25) Find the equation for line passing through $(2, -4)$ and $(5, 1)$.

   A. $-2x - 5y = 22$

   B. $3y - 5x = -22$

   C. $-3x + 10y = 12$

   D. $5y + 3x = -22$

26) If $x = -5$ and $y = 7$, calculate the value of $\dfrac{x^2+7}{y-3}$.

   A. $\dfrac{1}{8}$

   B. -8

   C. 8

   D. 4

27) The table shows the parking rates for the outside terminal area at an airport.

Ethan parked at the lot for $3\frac{1}{2}$ hours. How much did he owe?

A. $8.65

B. $7.65

C. $7.7

D. $7.85

2 hours	$3.20
Each 30 minutes after 2 hours	$1.5
24-hours Discount rate	$40

28) What is the value of x in term of c and d $\frac{c-d}{dx} = \frac{2}{7}$? (c and d>0)

A. $\frac{7}{2}(\frac{c}{d} - 1)$

B. $\frac{7}{2}(1 - \frac{c}{d})$

C. $\frac{2}{7}\left(\frac{c}{d} - 1\right)$

D. $\frac{2}{7}(1 - \frac{c}{d})$

29) Factor the equation $9x^4 - 4x^2$.

A. $2x^2(3x + 2)$

B. $x^2(2x + 3)(x - 3)$

C. $x^2(3x - 1)(x + 3)$

D. $x^2(3x - 2)(3x + 2)$

30) Which of the following are the solutions to the equation $x^2 - 14x + 48 = 0$?

    A. $-6, 8$

    B. $8, 6$

    C. $-8, -6$

    D. $6, -8$

31) Which of the following equations best represents the line in the graph below?

    A. $y = \frac{1}{5} x + 4$

    B. $y = x + 5$

    C. $y = \frac{1}{5} x - 5$

    D. $y = 5x + 1$

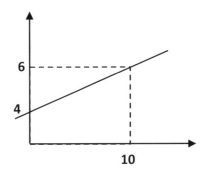

32) If $-3x + 2y = -2$ and $4x - 3y = 5$, what is the value of x?

    A. 7

    B. 1

    C. -2

    D. -4

33) lengths of Two sides of a triangle are 8 and 5. Which of the following could Not be the measure of third side?

    A. 2

    B. 4

    C. 10

    D. 12

34) The following data set is given: 111, 140, 127, 165, 159, 120

Adding which number to the set will increase its mean?

A. 134

B. 129

C. 132

D. 148

35) An award for best education improvement is awarded annually to a winning

US state, and the winners from 2002 to 2011 are given in the table below. Find

the mode of this set of states.

Year	2002	2003	2004	2005	2006	2007	2008	2009	2010	2011
State	New Jersey	New York	Oregon	New York	Oregon	California	Oregon	Ohio	Oregon	New York

A. Ohio and Oregon

B. California and Ohio

C. New York and Oregon

D. New Jersey and California

36) How long is a distance of 8 km if measured on a map with a scale of

1:50,000?

A. 14

B. 16

C. 8

D. 3

37) What is the area of a square, if its side measures $\sqrt{13}$ m?

    A. $\sqrt{13}$

    B. $3\sqrt{13}$

    C. $4\sqrt{13}$

    D. 13

38) What is the answer of the following equation $2x^4y^4\,(3x^3y^3)^4 =$?

    A. $81x^{11}y^{11}$

    B. $162x^{16}y^{16}$

    C. $46x^{10}y^8$

    D. $112x^8y^8$

39) The circle graph below shows the type of pizza that people prefer for lunch. If 220 people were surveyed, how many people preferred Margherita?

    A. 65

    B. 50

    C. 55

    D. 20

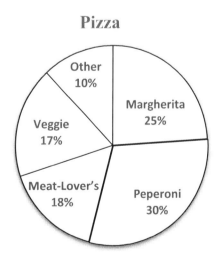

Pizza

40) Rosie is x years old. She is 3 years older than her twin brothers Milan and

Marcel. What is the mean age of the three children?

A. $x + 2$

B. $x - 3$

C. $x + 3$

D. $x - 2$

41) a is inversely proportional to $(2b - 5)$. If a = 8 and b = 9, express a in terms

of b.

A. $a = 2b - 18$

B. $a = 108(2b - 5)$

C. $a = \frac{104}{2b-5}$

D. $a = \frac{2b-5}{104}$

42) A baseball has a volume of 36π. What is the length of the diameter?

A. 15

B. 6

C. 3

D. 12

43) 154 is What percent of 140?

A. 110 %

B. 60 %

C. 120 %

D. 220 %

44) A phone manufacturer makes 18,000 phone a year. The company randomly selects 600 of the phones to sample for inspection. The company discovers that there are 5 faulty phones in the sample. Based on the sample, how many of the 18,000 total phones are likely to be faulty?

A. 300

B. 50

C. 250

D. 150

45) Emma and Mia buy a total of 28 books. Emma bought 4 more books than Mia did. How many books did Emma buy?

A. 24

B. 16

C. 12

D. 8

46) A bag contains 11 white balls, 6 red balls and 7 black balls. A ball is picked from the bag at random. Find the probability of picking a red ball?

A. 1.25

B. 2.25

C. 0.45

D. 0.25

47) The radius of the following cylinder is 4 inches, and its height are 9 inches.

What is the surface area of the cylinder in square inches? (π=3.14)

A. 326.56

B. 366.5

C. 5.56

D. 36.65

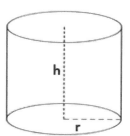

48) Find the length of the unknown side.

A. 36 ft

B. 26 ft

C. 35 ft

D. 38 ft

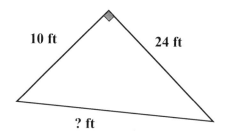

49) The line n has a slope of $\frac{a}{b}$, where a and b are integers. What is the slope of a line that is perpendicular to line n?

A. $-\frac{a}{b}$

B. $\frac{a}{b}$

C. $\frac{b}{a}$

D. $-\frac{b}{a}$

50) For what value(s) of x is the following equation true: $3x^2 - 18x + 27 = 0$?

    A. $3, 6$

    B. $+3$

    C. -3

    D. ± 3

51) Solve the linear inequality: $-\dfrac{(7x-3)}{3} + 5 \geq 13$

    A. $x \leq -3$

    B. $x > -3$

    C. $x \geq -3$

    D. $x < -3$

52) Evaluate: $\dfrac{(x^2+4x+3)}{(3x^2-12x+12)} \div \dfrac{(x^2-2x-3)}{(x^2-5x+6)} = ?$

    A. $\dfrac{x+3}{2x+6}$

    B. $\dfrac{2(x-3)}{x-6}$

    C. $\dfrac{x+3}{3x-6}$

    D. $\dfrac{x+6}{x-6}$

53) In a store, 38% of customers are female. If the total number of customers is

750, then how many male customers are dealing with the store?

A. 421

B. 726

C. 465

D. 356

54) If 66.33 kg is divided into two parts, in a ratio of 8:3, how many kg is the

smaller share?

A. 48.24 kg

B. 18.09 kg

C. 1.89 kg

D. 19.09 kg

55) Express as a single fraction in its simplest form: $\dfrac{5}{(x+2)} - \dfrac{2}{(4x-1)} = ?$

A. $\dfrac{18x-9}{(x+2)(4x-1)}$

B. $\dfrac{9x-18}{(x+2)(4x-1)}$

C. $\dfrac{15x-17}{4x+2}$

D. $\dfrac{-17}{4x-1}$

56) Ryan is x years old, and her sister Mitzi is $(6x - 20)$ years old. Given that Mitzi is twice as old as Ryan, what is Mitzi's age?

   A. 7

   B. 11

   C. 10

   D. 14

57) The set of possible values of p is $\{3, 5, 11\}$. What is the set of possible values of h if $2h = 5p + 1$?

   A. {6,17,25}

   B. {8,14,26}

   C. {8, 13, 28}

   D. {6,11,28}

58) In the infinitely repeating decimal below, 4 is the second digit in the repeating pattern. What is the 764th digit? $\frac{1}{21} = \overline{0.047619}$

   A. 4

   B. 7

   C. 9

   D. 0

59) $\frac{1}{7} = (?) \frac{5}{14}$

    A. 70%

    B. 65%

    C. 60%

    D. 40%

60) Consider the following series: 1, 3, 5, 6, 9, 14. What number should come next?

    A. 25

    B. 19

    C. 20

    D. 23

61) Evaluate: $(3y - 5x)(x + 2y)$?

    A. $-6x^2 - 5xy + 7y^2$

    B. $6x^2 - 7xy - 5y^2$

    C. $-5x^2 - 7xy + 6y^2$

    D. $5x^2 - 7xy + 5y^2$

62) Solve for y: $4.23 - 0.5y = -0.43$

    A. 8.23

    B. 3.73

    C. 9.32

    D. 6.25

63) Steven wants to make a platform that is 5 feet wide and 14 feet long. If he uses boards that measure 24 inches wide by 5 feet long, how many boards will he need to complete the job?

A. 35

B. 7

C. 12

D. 2

64) A cube has a side length of 90 cm, what is its volume in cubic meters?

$(100\ cm = 1\ m)$

A. 1.279

B. 1.81

C. 0.81

D. 0.729

"End of HSPT Practice Test 3."

HSPT Practice Test 4

Mathematics

Total Number of Questions: 64 Questions

Total time: 45 Minutes

You may NOT use a calculator for this test.

Administered *Month Year*

1) What is the sum of the smallest prime number and five times the largest negative even integer?

   A. -10

   B. 14

   C. -8

   D. -12

2) Sam's incomes and expenditures for the first season of the last year are given in the table below. In which month were her savings the highest?

   A. January

   B. March

   C. February

Month	Income	Cost
January	$3,740	$2,202
February	$3,855	$1,985
March	$3,970	$2,005

   D. All months were the same.

3) What is the number a, if the result of adding a to 29 is the same as subtracting $4a$ from 244?

   A. -59

   B. 34

   C. 122

   D. 43

4) Solve these fractions and reduce to its simplest terms: $8\frac{7}{24} - 6\frac{2}{3} + 2\frac{5}{6} =$

A. $4\frac{11}{24}$

B. $-4\frac{7}{24}$

C. $\frac{7}{8}$

D. $5\frac{3}{8}$

5) Calculate, $3^3 + 3 + 3^0 = ?$

A. 3^4

B. 30

C. 31

D. 35

6) Which decimal is equivalent to $\frac{153}{170}$?

A. 0.109

B. 1.09

C. 0.09

D. 0.9

7) The price of a shirt increased from \$30 to \$32.10. What is the percentage increase in the price?

A. 7%

B. 0.7%

C. 0.93%

D. 1.7%

8) Find the solution set of the following equation: $|2x - 3| = 7$

   A. $\{5, -2\}$

   B. $\{2, -5\}$

   C. $\{2\}$

   D. $\{-5, -2\}$

9) What is the solution to the pair of equations below? $\begin{cases} 2x - 5y = 16 \\ 2x + y = 4 \end{cases}$

   A. $x = 0$ and $y = -3$

   B. $x = -3$ and $y = 0$

   C. $x = 3$ and $y = -2$

   D. $x = 3$ and $y = -3$

10) The train each 30 minutes passes an average 5 stations. At this rate, how many stations will it pass in three hours.

   A. 20

   B. 30

   C. 45

   D. 60

11) If Sofia buys a shirt marked down 16 percent from its $160 while Natalia buys

the same shirt mark down only 11 percent, how much more does Natalia pay

for the shirt?

A. $80

B. $4.8

C. $16

D. $8

12) Find the circumference of the circle in terms of π.

A. 9π in.

B. 72π in.

C. 36 π in.

D. 112π in.

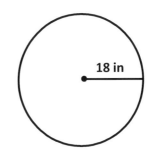

13) Find the volume of rectangular prism below?

A. 1,880 in^3

B. 1,080 in^3

C. 2,280 in^3

D. 285 in^3

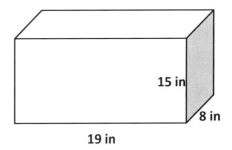

14) What is $\sqrt[4]{5^{-8}}$ in simplest form?

   A. $\dfrac{1}{2,250}$

   B. $\dfrac{1}{125}$

   C. $\dfrac{1}{5}$

   D. $\dfrac{1}{25}$

15) Which statement correctly describes the value of N in the equation below?

   $7(4N - 10) = 4(7N - 15)$?

   A. N has no correct solutions.

   B. N=1 is one solution.

   C. N has infinitely many correct solutions.

   D. N=0 is one solution.

16) What is the maximum amount of grain, the silo can hold, in cubic feet?

   A. $1,620\pi \ m^3$

   B. $405\pi \ m^3$

   C. $810\pi \ m^3$

   D. $1,200\pi \ m^3$

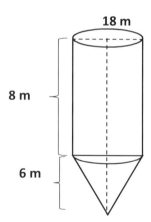

17) What is 7.25×10^{-5} in standard form?

    A. $-72,500$

    B. -0.0000725

    C. $\dfrac{1}{725,000}$

    D. 0.0000725

18) What is the value of x in the triangle?

    A. $64°$

    B. $130°$

    C. $50°$

    D. $60°$

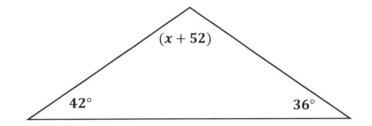

19) Find the length of the unknown side.

    A. 22 ft

    B. 20 ft

    C. 18 ft

    D. 12 ft

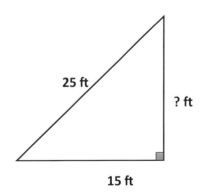

20) A store sells all of its products at a price 12% greater than the price the store paid for the product. How much does the store sell a product if the store paid $150 for it?

   A. $180

   B. $160

   C. $168

   D. $38

21) What is the area of shaded region?

   A. 95

   B. 35

   C. 130

   D. 165

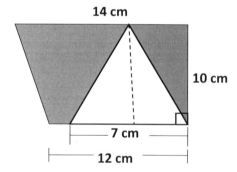

22) if $xy - 8x = 54$ and $y - 8 = 6$, then $x =$?

   A. 8

   B. 14

   C. 6

   D. 9

23) Which is the value of x in the equation $\frac{x}{4} = x - 6$?

    A. 4

    B. 6

    C. 8

    D. 12

24) What is the value of x, If $-5x + 4y = 7$ and $-4x + 3y = 5$?

    A. -2

    B. 0

    C. 3

    D. 1

25) What is the probability of Not spinning at F?

    A. $\frac{5}{8}$

    B. $\frac{3}{8}$

    C. $\frac{1}{8}$

    D. $\frac{7}{8}$

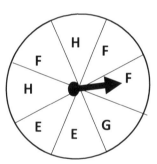

26) Ella bought 32 movies for $5.04 per movie. Which equation shows the BEST estimate of the total cost?

    A. 30 × $6 = $180

    B. 30 × $5 = $150

    C. 32× $5 = $160

    D. 32 × $6 = $192

27) A pick-up truck travels 50 mile on 7 L of gasoline when driven on a smooth road. If the cost of gasoline is $1.40/L, which is the cost of 1,500 mile of highway (smooth)?

A. $141

B. $1,249

C. $129

D. $294

28) A position of subway station and Grace's house shown by a grid. The station is located at $(-6, -9)$, and her house is located at $(2, -3)$. What is the distance between her house and the subway stop?

A. 6

B. 10

C. $10\sqrt{2}$

D. 15

29) For the following set of numbers find the median.

225, 75, 280, 89, 198, 124, 512.

A. 198

B. 124

C. 225

D. 89

30) What is solution to the equation $\sqrt{4x - 7} = 9$?

   A. -18

   B. -14

   C. 10

   D. 22

31) The equation $x = 4y - 8$ has a y-intercept of?

   A. 2

   B. -2

   C. $\frac{1}{2}$

   D. $-\frac{1}{2}$

32) If $3^{2x} = 729$, then $x = ?$

   A. 4

   B. 6

   C. 3

   D. 2

33) Which is the smallest positive integer which is divisible by both 18 and 64.

   A. 108

   B. 54

   C. 576

   D. 124

34) A cube has total surface area of 96 cm^2. what is the volume of the cube in cm^3?

    A. 8

    B. 64

    C. 36

    D. 108

35) Which is the value of x^2, if $x^2 + 2x = 35$?

    A. 12

    B. -7

    C. 36

    D. 25

36) Each of 5 pitchers can contain up to $\frac{3}{5}$ L of water. If each of the pitcher is at least the half full, which of the following expressions represents the total amount of water, W, contained on all 5 pitchers?

    A. $2.5 < w < 5$

    B. $1.5 < w < 5$

    C. $0.5 < w < 3$

    D. $1.5 < w < 3$

37) Ages of the players on a volleyball team is given. Which is the range of their

ages? 47, 32, 17, 65, 22, 40, 28, 57, 20, 18, 56, 39

    A. 38

    B. 19

    C. 48

    D. 52

38) Find the area of the circle to the nearest tenth. Use 3.14 for π.

    A. 201

    B. 202

    C. 200.9

    D. 109

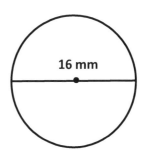

16 mm

39) What is the simplest form of the expression $\dfrac{2x^2-15x+7}{4(x^2-\frac{1}{4})}$?

    A. $\dfrac{x+7}{2(x-\frac{1}{2})}$

    B. $\dfrac{x-7}{2x+1}$

    C. $\dfrac{x+7}{2x+1}$

    D. $\dfrac{x-7}{x-2}$

40) What is the value of $\left(\frac{1}{3}\right)^{-4}$?

    A. $\frac{1}{81}$

    B. -81

    C. $-\frac{1}{81}$

    D. 81

41) What is the simplest form of the expression $\frac{(5x^{-3}y^4)^3}{100y^{-2}z^2}$, (using positive exponent)?

    A. $\frac{4y^{14}z}{59}$

    B. $\frac{5y^{14}}{4x^9z^2}$

    C. $\frac{5x^8z^2}{4zy^8}$

    D. $\frac{x^{14}}{y^9}$

42) Some fruit sells for \$30 per kilograms. What is the price in cent per gram?

    A. 0.003

    B. 0.3

    C. 0.03

    D. 3

43) The price of water triples every 5 years. If the price of water on January 1st, 2012, is $6 per gallon, what is the equation that would be used to calculate the price(P) of water on January 1st, 2007?

A. $6P = 6$

B. $\dfrac{P}{6} = 3$

C. $3p = 6$

D. $6P = 3$

44) The line $4y + 5 = 20x + 9$ and $5y + 4 = x + 7$ are?

A. Perpendicular

B. Parallel

C. The same line

D. Neither parallel nor perpendicular

45) A rectangular box measures $5\frac{1}{3}$ feet by $8\frac{2}{5}$ feet. It is divided into four equal parts. What is the area of one of those parts?

A. 11

B. 9.2

C. 11.2

D. 22.4

46) Find the slope of the line.

A. $\frac{1}{2}$

B. $\frac{1}{3}$

C. 2

D. $-\frac{1}{4}$

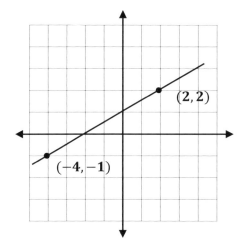

47) Amelia cuts a piece of birthday cake as shown below. What is the volume of

the piece of cake?

A. $425\ cm^3$

B. $375\ cm^3$

C. $750\ cm^3$

D. $250\ cm^3$

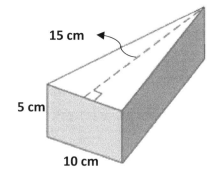

48) Let $f(x) = 4x - 7$. If $f(a) = -19$ and $f(b) = 9$, then what is $f(a + b)$?

A. 3

B. 5

C. -3

D. -5

49) Given that $28x = 12y$, find the ratio $x: y$.

    A. $5:9$

    B. $4:11$

    C. $6:5$

    D. $3:7$

50) What is the number of sides of a regular polygon whose interior angles are $168°$ each? (Remember, the sum of exterior angles of any polygon is $360°$).

    A. 6

    B. 30

    C. 22

    D. 12

51) Frank is now 5 times as old as his son Jim. Four years ago, the product of their ages was 21. Find their present ages.

    A. Frank: 40 years; Jim: 8 years.

    B. Frank: 20 years; Jim: 4 years.

    C. Frank: 25 years; Jim: 5 years.

    D. Frank: 30 years; Jim: 6 years.

52) Solve the equation and choose the best answer: $\frac{d}{4} = \frac{16}{d}$

   A. −4

   B. −8

   C. 4

   D. 32

53) In a competition, three teams, FT, RT and GT, scored a total of 220 points. If FT scored 25% of this total and RT scored four times as many points as GT, what were the number of points scored by RT?

   A. 132

   B. 102

   C. 55

   D. 33

54) The sum of two consecutive integers is −23. If 5 is added to the smaller integer and 3 is subtracted from the larger integer, what is the product of the two resulting integers?

   A. 98

   B. 82

   C. 120

   D. 64

55) A sports store has a container of handballs: 25 blue, 18 red, 8 yellow, 19 white, and 7 green. If one ball is picked from the container at random, what is the probability that it will be green?

A. $\frac{1}{7}$

B. $\frac{1}{11}$

C. $\frac{1}{17}$

D. $\frac{1}{22}$

56) $8 + (3n + 11) - (10n + 5)$

A. $14 - 7n$

B. $12 + 5n$

C. $-14 - 7n$

D. $-7 + 10n$

57) Jimmy must read 106 pages for school this weekend. It took him 15 minutes to read the first 8 pages. At this rate, how much additional time will it take him to finish the reading?

A. $4\frac{3}{20}$

B. $4\frac{5}{12}$

C. $3\frac{1}{16}$

D. $5\frac{1}{8}$

58) If the line m is parallel to the side BC of ABC, what is angle n?

A. 135

B. 65

C. 35

D. 165

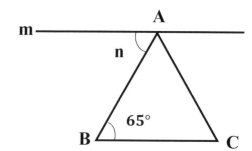

59) The cost of 1 pound of fruit is $3.60. How many pounds of food can be bought

for $18.00?

A. 5.50 pounds

B. 0.50 pounds

C. 50.0 pounds

D. 5.00 pounds

60) Given that 20 cm on a map represents 4 km on the ground, calculate the distance

in km between two points, which are 32 cm apart on the map.

A. 4.6 km

B. 6.4 km

C. 64 km

D. 46 km

61) What is the percent equivalent of 0.056?

A. 0.056%

B. 56%

C. 5.60%

D. 0.56%

62) When a number is subtracted from 90 and the result is divided by 7, the answer obtained is twice the original number. What is the number?

A. 6

B. 10

C. 15

D. 30

63) Tiffani's base salary last year was \$52,000, not including her bonus. When she opened her HR profile, she saw that her total compensation added up to \$64,000. This total included her bonus, as well as health benefits equivalent to 15% of her base salary. What percentage of Tiffani's base salary plus benefits was her bonus (Rounded to the nearest tenth)?

A. 4.5

B. 0.8

C. 7.0

D. 13.2

64) The operation is defined as $a \ @ \ b = a - 2ab$

The operation # is defined as $a\#b = a - 4b^2$

If $f(x) = 2x^2 - 14$, what is the value of $\left(f(-3) @ f(2)\right)\#f(-3)$?

A. -34

B. -12

C. -140

D. 64

"End of HSPT Practice Test 4."

HSPT Practice Test 5

Mathematics

Total Number of Questions: 64 Questions

Total time: 45 Minutes

You may NOT use a calculator for this test.

Administered *Month Year*

1) How many even integers are between $\frac{-26}{3}$ and $\frac{75}{8}$?

    A. 8

    B. 5

    C. 9

    D. 11

2) Which expression correctly represents the distance between the two points shown on the number line?

    A. $-8 - 7$

    B. $|-8 + 7|$

    C. $-8 + 7$

    D. $|8 + 7|$

3) In the triangle ABC, if angle B and angle C both equal 60°, then what is the length of side BC?

    A. 4 cm

    B. 8 cm

    C. 12 cm

    D. 16 cm

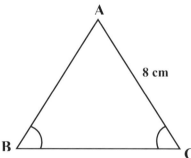

4) Which of the following represents the sum of the factors of 24?

   A. 60

   B. 50

   C. 46

   D. 35

5) Alice read $\frac{1}{6}$ of her book on Saturday and $\frac{3}{8}$ of her book on Sunday. What fraction of her book remains to be read?

   A. $\frac{11}{12}$

   B. $\frac{11}{24}$

   C. $\frac{13}{24}$

   D. $\frac{13}{48}$

6) Complete the following pattern. 8,000; 400; _____; 1; _____; _____.

   A. 50; 0.05; 0.001

   B. 20; 0.05; 0.0025

   C. 200; 0.02; 0.004

   D. 100; 0.01; 0.0001

7) Find the greatest common factor of 16, 27, and 20.

   A. 1

   B. 4

   C. 8

   D. 9

8) Which equation can be equal "4 more than the ratio of a number to 5 is equal to 7 less than the number"?

A. $4x - 5 = 7 - x$

B. $4 + \frac{x}{5} = x - 7$

C. $\frac{4}{5}x - 7 = 5x$

D. $4 + 5x = 7 - x$

9) Arrange the following fractions in order from least to greatest.

$$\frac{3}{7}, \frac{5}{9}, \frac{1}{3}, \frac{19}{21}, \frac{11}{18}$$

A. $\frac{1}{3}, \frac{3}{7}, \frac{5}{9}, \frac{11}{18}, \frac{19}{21}$

B. $\frac{5}{9}, \frac{3}{7}, \frac{1}{3}, \frac{11}{18}, \frac{19}{21}$

C. $\frac{19}{21}, \frac{11}{18}, \frac{5}{9}, \frac{3}{7}, \frac{1}{3}$

D. $\frac{11}{18}, \frac{19}{21}, \frac{1}{3}, \frac{3}{7}, \frac{5}{9}$

10) Elena earns $9.20 an hour and worked 35 hours. Her brother earns $11.50 an hour. How many hours would her brother need to work to equal Elena's earnings over 40 hours?

A. 15.22

B. 28

C. 35

D. 80.50

11) In a library, 40% of the books are fiction and the rest are non-fiction. Given that there are 1,200 more non-fiction books than fiction books, what is the total number of books in the library?

A. 2,000

B. 5,000

C. 6,000

D. 4,000

12) A map has the scale of 5 cm to 1 km. What is the actual area of a lake on ground which is represented as an area of $80\ cm^2$ on the map?

A. $16\ km^2$

B. $3.2\ km^2$

C. $16\ cm^2$

D. $3.2\ cm^2$

13) $12.24 \div 0.4 =$

A. 3.06

B. 30.60

C. 30.06

D. 3.006

14) What is the circumference of a circle with a radius of 8 inches?

    A. $64\,\pi$

    B. $16\,\pi$

    C. $128\,\pi$

    D. $48\,\pi$

15) Alfred needs to calculate his monthly water bill. His family used 23,700 gallons at a rate of $0.95 per hundred gallons. Also, there is a monthly fee of $4.20 on each period. What is his total bill?

    A. $22,519.20

    B. $225.15

    C. $229.35

    D. $6.45

16) Simplify $\dfrac{(x^3-x^2)}{(x^2-x)} =$?

    A. x

    B. $x-1$

    C. $2x$

    D. $x(x-1)$

17) Which of the following expressions is undefined in the set of real numbers?

   A. $\sqrt[2]{148}$

   B. $\sqrt[3]{-27}$

   C. $\sqrt{-81}$

   D. $\sqrt[4]{16}$

18) If $f(x) = 5x^2$, and 3f(2a) = 540 then what could be the value of a?

   A. -3

   B. -1

   C. 1

   D. 3

19) Speed of a train is 110 mile per hour for 2 hours and 30 minutes. How many miles did the train travel?

   A. 275

   B. 256

   C. 253

   D. 270

20) Solve $10x - 7 \leq 6x + 5$

   A. $x \leq -3$

   B. $x \geq -3$

   C. $x \leq 3$

   D. $x \geq 3$

21) What is the value of 3^4?

    A. $(3+3)^2$

    B. 9^2

    C. $3(3^2)$

    D. $3^2 + 3^2$

22) Shane Williams puts \$3,800 into a saving bank account that pays simple interest of 4.5%. How much interest will she earn after 3 years?

    A. \$5,130

    B. \$ 1,710

    C. \$513

    D. \$171

23) Three angles join to form a straight angle. One angle measure 55°. Other angle measures 30°. What is the measure of third angle?

    A. 5°

    B. 15°

    C. 35°

    D. 95°

24) Evaluate $\frac{32x^5y^7z^{-2}}{12\,x^2y^9z^0}$.

    A. $\frac{4x^3y^2}{3\,z^2}$

    B. $\frac{4x^3z^2}{3\,y^2}$

    C. $\frac{8x^3}{3\,y^2z^2}$

    D. $\frac{8y^2}{3\,x^3z^2}$

25) Find the equation for line passing through $(2, -1)$ and $(4,2)$.

    A. $-3x - 2y = 10$

    B. $2y - 3x = -8$

    C. $-3x + 2y = 10$

    D. $2y + 3x = -8$

26) If $x = -2$ and $y = 2$, calculate the value of $\frac{x^2+5}{y+1}$.

    A. $\frac{1}{3}$

    B. -3

    C. 3

    D. 2

27) The table shows the parking rates for the outside terminal area at an airport.

Ethan parked at the lot for $3\frac{1}{2}$ hours. How much did he owe?

A. $4:25

B. $3:50

C. $5:75

D. $6:50

2 hours	$3.5
Each 30 minutes after 2 hours	$0.75
24-hours Discount rate	$40

28) What is the value of x in term of c and d $\frac{c-d}{dx} = \frac{2}{3}$? (c and d>0)

A. $\frac{3}{2}(\frac{c}{d} - 1)$

B. $\frac{3}{2}(1 - \frac{c}{d})$

C. $\frac{2}{3}(\frac{c}{d} - 1)$

D. $\frac{2}{3}(1 - \frac{c}{d})$

29) Factor the equation $x^3 - x$.

A. $3x(x - 1)$

B. $x(x + 2)(x - 1)$

C. $x(x - 2)(x + 1)$

D. $x(x - 1)(x + 1)$

30) Which of the following are the solutions to the equation $x^2 - 10x + 24 = 0$?

    A. $-12, 2$

    B. $6, 4$

    C. $-4, -6$

    D. $12, -2$

31) Which of the following equations best represents the line in the graph below?

    A. $y = \frac{1}{2}x + 2$

    B. $y = x + 5$

    C. $y = \frac{1}{2}x - 2$

    D. $y = x + 2$

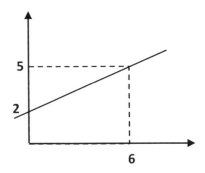

32) If $-3x + 4y = -5$ and $2x - 5y = 8$, what is the value of x?

    A. 2

    B. 2.60

    C. -8

    D. -1

33) lengths of Two sides of a triangle are 5 and 8. Which of the following could Not be the measure of third side?

    A. 2

    B. 4

    C. 9

    D. 11

34) The following data set is given: 134, 118, 148, 184, 159, 151.

Adding which number to the set will increase its mean?

A. 129

B. 139

C. 149

D. 159

35) An award for best education improvement is awarded annually to a winning

US state, and the winners from 2002 to 2011 are given in the table below. Find

the mode of this set of states.

Year	2002	2003	2004	2005	2006	2007	2008	2009	2010	2011
State	New York	Ohio	New Jersey	New York	Ohio	California	Ohio	Oregon	New York	New Jersey

A. New York and New Jersey

B. California and Oregon

C. Ohio and New York

D. Ohio and California

36) How long is a distance of 6 km if measured on a map with a scale of

1:50,000?

A. 6

B. 12

C. 16

D. 18

37) What is the area of a square, if its side measures $\sqrt{5}$ m?

    A. $\sqrt{5}$

    B. $5\sqrt{5}$

    C. $2\sqrt{5}$

    D. 5

38) What is the answer of the following equation $2x^4 y^3 (4x^3 y^0)^3 =$?

    A. $24x^{10}y^6$

    B. $128x^{13}y^3$

    C. $128x^{13}y^6$

    D. $24x^{13}y^3$

39) The circle graph below shows the type of pizza that people prefer for lunch. If 250 people were surveyed, how many people preferred Meat lovers?

    A. 18

    B. 25

    C. 45

    D. 55

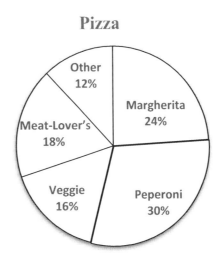

Pizza

Other 12%

Margherita 24%

Meat-Lover's 18%

Veggie 16%

Peperoni 30%

40) Rosie is x years old. She is 3 years older than her twin brothers Milan and Marcel. What is the mean age of the three children?

   A. $x + 2$

   B. $x - 3$

   C. $x + 3$

   D. $x - 2$

41) a is inversely proportional to $(2b - 5)$. If a = 15 and b = 7, express a in terms of b.

   A. $a = 2b - 5$

   B. $a = 105(2b - 5)$

   C. $a = \frac{135}{2b-5}$

   D. $a = \frac{2b-5}{135}$

42) A baseball has a volume of 36π. What is the length of the diameter?

   A. 3

   B. 6

   C. 9

   D. 12

43) 221 is What percent of 170?

   A. 130 %

   B. 77 %

   C. 30 %

   D. 123 %

44) A phone manufacturer makes 12,000 phone a year. The company randomly selects 200 of the phones to sample for inspection. The company discovers that there are 3 faulty phones in the sample. Based on the sample, how many of the 12,000 total phones are likely to be faulty?

A. 20

B. 60

C. 120

D. 180

45) Emma and Mia buy a total of 17 books. Emma bought 5 more books than Mia did. How many books did Emma buy?

A. 7

B. 11

C. 12

D. 15

46) A bag contains 5 white balls, 4 red balls and 7 black balls. A ball is picked from the bag at random. Find the probability of picking a red ball?

A. 1.25

B. 0.28

C. 0.33

D. 0.25

47) The radius of the following cylinder is 6 inches, and its height are 9 inches.

What is the surface area of the cylinder in square inches? (π=3.14)

A. 565.2

B. 109.9

C. 1,130

D. 94.2

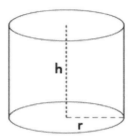

48) Find the length of the unknown side.

A. 17.5 ft

B. 25 ft

C. 35 ft

D. 625 ft

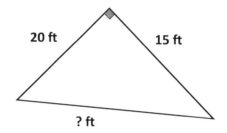

49) The line n has a slope of $\frac{c}{d}$, where c and d are integers. What is the slope of a

line that is perpendicular to line n?

A. $\frac{c}{d}$

B. $-\frac{c}{d}$

C. $\frac{d}{c}$

D. $-\frac{d}{c}$

50) For what value(s) of x is the following equation true: $3x^2 - 18x + 27 = 0$?

    A. $3, 6$

    B. $+3$

    C. -3

    D. ± 3

51) Solve the linear inequality: $-\dfrac{(5x-8)}{4} + 9 \geq 11$

    A. $x \leq 0$

    B. $x > 0$

    C. $x \geq 0$

    D. $x < 0$

52) Evaluate: $\dfrac{(x^2+5x+6)}{(2x^2-8x+8)} \div \dfrac{(x^2+2x-3)}{(x^2-3x+2)} = ?$

    A. $\dfrac{x+2}{2x-2}$

    B. $\dfrac{2(x+2)}{x-2}$

    C. $\dfrac{x-2}{2x-4}$

    D. $\dfrac{x+2}{x-2}$

53) In a store, 38% of customers are female. If the total number of customers is

950, then how many male customers are dealing with the store?

A. 228

B. 361

C. 589

D. 675

54) If 54.5 kg is divided into two parts, in a ratio of 8:3, how many kg is the

smaller share?

A. 18.17 kg

B. 14.86 kg

C. 2.67 kg

D. 6.81 kg

55) Express as a single fraction in its simplest form: $\frac{5}{(x-2)} - \frac{6}{(3x+1)} = ?$

A. $\frac{9x+17}{(x-2)(3x+1)}$

B. $\frac{9x-17}{(x-2)(3x+1)}$

C. $\frac{9x+17}{3x-2}$

D. $\frac{-1}{3x-2}$

56) Ryan is x years old, and her sister Mitzi is $(5x - 18)$ years old. Given that Mitzi is twice as old as Ryan, what is Mitzi's age?

   A. 6

   B. 9

   C. 12

   D. 18

57) The set of possible values of p is {2,5,11}. What is the set of possible values of h if $3h = 2p + 2$?

   A. {2,5,11}

   B. {6,15,33}

   C. {2,4,8}

   D. {6,12,24}

58) In the infinitely repeating decimal below, 1 is the first digit in the repeating pattern. What is the 391st digit? $\frac{1}{7} = \overline{0.142857}$

   A. 1

   B. 4

   C. 8

   D. 5

59) $\frac{2}{5} = (?)\frac{5}{7}$

   A. 100%

   B. 65%

   C. 78%

   D. 56%

60) Consider the following series: 7, 5, 2, 9, 14, 16. What number should come next?

   A. 18

   B. 21

   C. 25

   D. 30

61) Evaluate: $(3y - x)(x - 2y)$?

   A. $-x^2 - 2xy + 6y^2$

   B. $x^2 - 5xy + 6y^2$

   C. $-x^2 + 5xy - 6y^2$

   D. $-x^2 + xy - 6y^2$

62) Solve for y: $1.87 - 0.6y = -0.86$

   A. 4.25

   B. 4.65

   C. 4.55

   D. 3.75

63) Steven wants to make a platform that is 8 feet wide and 9 feet long. If he uses boards that measure 6 inches wide by 4 feet long, how many boards will he need to complete the job?

A. 72

B. 36

C. 24

D. 3

64) A cube has a side length of 140 cm, what is its volume in cubic meters?

$(100\ cm = 1\ m)$

A. 4.20

B. 1.96

C. 2.80

D. 2.744

"End of HSPT Practice Test 5."

HSPT Practice Test 6

Mathematics

Total Number of Questions: 64 Questions

Total time: 45 Minutes

You may NOT use a calculator for this test.

Administered *Month Year*

1) What is the sum of the smallest prime number and three times the largest negative even integer?

A. −2

B. 0

C. −4

D. −6

2) Sam's incomes and expenditures for the first season of the last year are given in the table below. In which month were her savings the highest?

A. January

B. February

C. March

D. All months were the same.

Month	Income	Cost
January	$3,025	$1,870
February	$3,405	$1,916
March	$3,280	$1,962

3) What is the number a, if the result of adding a to 42 is the same as subtracting $3a$ from 230?

A. −94

B. 68

C. 188

D. 47

4) Solve these fractions and reduce to its simplest terms: $4\frac{1}{21} - 5\frac{4}{7} + 2\frac{1}{3} =$

   A. $\frac{17}{21}$

   B. $-1\frac{4}{21}$

   C. $\frac{6}{7}$

   D. $1\frac{2}{3}$

5) Calculate, $3^3 + 3^2 + 3 =?$

   A. 9^6

   B. 18

   C. 39

   D. 729

6) Which decimal is equivalent to $\frac{108}{270}$?

   A. 0.108

   B. 0.27

   C. 0.04

   D. 0.4

7) The price of a shirt increased from \$30 to \$31.50. What is the percentage increase in the price?

   A. 5%

   B. 0.5%

   C. 0.95%

   D. 1.5%

8) Find the solution set of the following equation: $|2x - 3| = 5$

    A. $\{4, -1\}$

    B. $\{1, -1\}$

    C. $\{5\}$

    D. $\{-4, 1\}$

9) What is the solution to the pair of equations below? $\begin{cases} x - 3y = 1 \\ 2x + y = 2 \end{cases}$

    A. $x = 4$ and $y = 1$

    B. $x = 0$ and $y = 1$

    C. $x = 1$ and $y = 0$

    D. $x = 1$ and $y = -3$

10) The train each 15 minutes passes an average 4 stations. At this rate, how many stations will it pass in two hours.

    A. 8

    B. 32

    C. 16

    D. 48

11) If Sofia buys a shirt marked down 8 percent from its $180 while Natalia buys

the same shirt mark down only 6 percent, how much more does Natalia pay

for the shirt?

A.$0.36

B.$1.80

C.$2

D.$3.60

12) Find the circumference of the circle in terms of π.

A.21.5π in.

B.43π in.

C.$86\ \pi$ in.

D.$1,849\pi$ in.

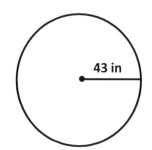

13) Find the volume of rectangular prism below?

A.$513\ in^3$

B.$1026\ in^3$

C.$2,052\ in^3$

D.$4,104\ in^3$

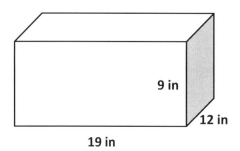

14) What is $\sqrt[4]{4^{-8}}$ in simplest form?

A. $\dfrac{1}{65,536}$

B. $\dfrac{1}{256}$

C. $\dfrac{1}{64}$

D. $\dfrac{1}{16}$

15) Which statement correctly describes the value of N in the equation below?

$4(7N - 12) = 7(4N - 12)$?

A. N has no correct solutions.

B. N=0 is one solution.

C. N has infinitely many correct solutions.

D. N=1 is one solution.

16) What is the maximum amount of grain, the silo can hold, in cubic feet?

A. $144\pi \ m^3$

B. $288\pi \ m^3$

C. $896\pi \ m^3$

D. $1,152\pi \ m^3$

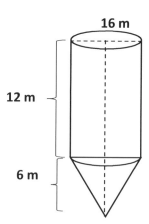

17) What is 3.21×10^{-4} in standard form?

A. –32,120

B. –0.000321

C. $\frac{1}{32,100}$

D. 0.000321

18) What is the value of x in the triangle?

A. 77°

B. 130°

C. 50°

D. 103°

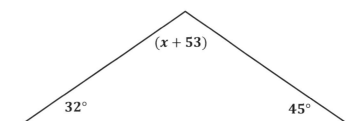

19) Find the length of the unknown side.

A. 23.3 ft

B. 16 ft

C. 256 ft

D. 8 ft

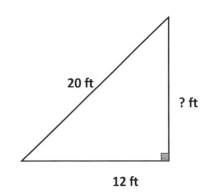

20) A store sells all of its products at a price 18% greater than the price the store

paid for the product. How much does the store sell a product if the store paid

$250 for it?

A. $268

B. $205

C. $295

D. $45

21) What is the area of shaded region?

A. 81

B. 54

C. 27

D. 18

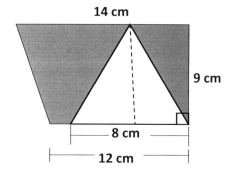

22) if $xy - 5x = 32$ and $y - 5 = 8$, then $x =$?

A. 32

B. 16

C. 8

D. 4

23) Which is the value of x in the equation $\frac{x}{3} = x - 4$?

    A. 1

    B. 2

    C. 3

    D. 6

24) What is the value of x, If $-5x + 2y = 20$ and $-4x + 3y = 9$?

    A. -3

    B. -4

    C. -5

    D. -6

25) What is the probability of Not spinning at F?

    A. $\frac{5}{8}$

    B. $\frac{3}{8}$

    C. $\frac{1}{3}$

    D. $\frac{1}{5}$

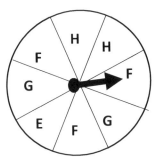

26) Ella bought 23 movies for $2.08 per movie. Which equation shows the BEST

estimate of the total cost?

    A. $20 \times \$2 = \$40$

    B. $20 \times \$3 = \$60$

    C. $23 \times \$2 = \$46$

    D. $23 \times \$3 = \$69$

27) A pick-up truck travels 75 mile on 12 L of gasoline when driven on a smooth

road. If the cost of gasoline is $1.05/L, which is the cost of 1,700 mile of

highway (smooth)?

A. $11,156.25

B. $1,785

C. $148.75

D. $285.60

28) A position of subway station and Grace's house shown by a grid. The station

is located at $(-2, -7)$, and her house is located at $(6, -1)$. What is the

distance between her house and the subway stop?

A. 8

B. 10

C. $8\sqrt{2}$

D. 6

29) For the following set of numbers find the median.

212, 122, 318, 122, 186, 165, 334.

A. 186

B. 122

C. 154

D. 342

30) What is solution to the equation $\sqrt{3x-1} = 4$?

A. -1

B. -5

C. 1

D. 5

31) The equation $x = 2y - 4$ has a y-intercept of?

A. 2

B. -4

C. $\frac{1}{2}$

D. $-\frac{1}{4}$

32) If $3^{2x} = 81$, then $x = ?$

A. 4

B. 3

C. 2

D. 1

33) Which is the smallest positive integer which is divisible by both 24 and 30.

A. 6

B. 60

C. 120

D. 240

34) A cube has total surface area of 54 cm². what is the volume of the cube in cm³?

   A. 81

   B. 27

   C. 9

   D. 3

35) Which is the value of x^2, if $x^2 + x = 30$?

   A. 16

   B. -25

   C. 30

   D. 36

36) Each of 5 pitchers can contain up to $\frac{3}{5}$ L of water. If each of the pitcher is at least the half full, which of the following expressions represents the total amount of water, W, contained on all 5 pitchers?

   A. $0.6 < w < 6$

   B. $0 < w < 1.5$

   C. $0 < w < 3$

   D. $1.5 < w < 3$

37) Ages of the players on a volleyball team is given. Which is the range of their ages? 34, 41, 35, 45, 32, 34, 31, 29, 40, 28, 37, 39

A. 5

B. 11

C. 17

D. 45

38) Find the area of the circle to the nearest tenth. Use 3.14 for π.

A. 153.9

B. 615.4

C. 44.0

D. 22

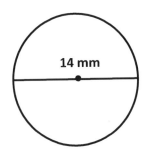

14 mm

39) What is the simplest form of the expression $\frac{2x^2-7x-4}{4(x^2-\frac{1}{4})}$?

A. $\frac{x+4}{4(x-\frac{1}{2})}$

B. $\frac{x-4}{2x-1}$

C. $\frac{x+4}{2x+1}$

D. $\frac{2x-1}{x-4}$

40) What is the value of $\left(\frac{1}{3}\right)^{-3}$?

A. $\frac{1}{27}$

B. -27

C. $-\frac{1}{27}$

D. 27

41) What is the simplest form of the expression $\frac{(5x^{-2}y^3)^2}{125y^{-2}z^{-1}}$, (using positive

exponent)?

A. $\frac{2y^8z^2}{25x^4}$

B. $\frac{y^8z}{5x^4}$

C. $\frac{2x^4}{25zy^8}$

D. $\frac{x^4}{5y^8z}$

42) Some fruit sells for $10 per kilograms. What is the price in cent per gram?

A. 0.001

B. 0.1

C. 0.01

D. 1

43) The price of water doubles every 5 years. If the price of water on January 1st, 2012, is \$2 per gallon, what is the equation that would be used to calculate the price(P) of water on January 1st, 2007?

A. $5P = 2$

B. $\dfrac{P}{2} = 2$

C. $2p = 2$

D. $2P = 5$

44) The line $2y - 1 = 4x + 5$ and $4y - 1 = 2x + 5$ are?

A. Parallel

B. Perpendicular

C. The same line

D. Neither parallel nor perpendicular

45) A rectangular box measures $9\frac{1}{2}$ feet by $7\frac{1}{5}$ feet. It is divided into four equal parts. What is the area of one of those parts?

A. 4.28

B. 15.80

C. 17.10

D. 68.40

46) Find the slope of the line.

A. $\frac{1}{2}$

B. $\frac{1}{3}$

C. 2

D. $-\frac{1}{2}$

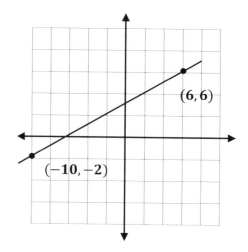

$(6,6)$

$(-10,-2)$

47) Amelia cuts a piece of birthday cake as shown below. What is the volume of the piece of cake?

A. $540\ cm^3$

B. $270\ cm^3$

C. $180\ cm^3$

D. $2{,}430\ cm^3$

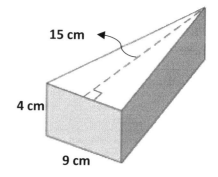

15 cm

4 cm

9 cm

48) Let $f(x) = 5x - 2$. If $f(a) = -12$ and $f(b) = 13$, then what is $f(a + b)$?

A. -2

B. 2

C. 3

D. -3

49) Given that $8x = 6y$, find the ratio $x:y$.

    A. $6:48$

    B. $8:48$

    C. $4:3$

    D. $3:4$

50) What is the number of sides of a regular polygon whose interior angles are $144°$ each? (Remember, the sum of exterior angles of any polygon is $360°$).

    A. 5

    B. 10

    C. 6

    D. 12

51) Frank is now 4 times as old as his son Jim. Five years ago, the product of their ages was 46. Find their present ages.

    A. Frank: 40 years; Jim: 10 years.

    B. Frank: 36 years; Jim: 9 years.

    C. Frank: 28 years; Jim: 7 years.

    D. Frank: 23 years; Jim: 2 years.

52) Solve the equation and choose the best answer: $\frac{d}{4} = \frac{16}{d}$

A. −4

B. −8

C. 16

D. 64

53) In a competition, three teams, FT, RT and GT, scored a total of 160 points. If FT scored 45% of this total and RT scored three times as many points as GT, what were the number of points scored by RT?

A. 66

B. 72

C. 6

D. 22

54) The sum of two consecutive integers is −15. If 1 is added to the smaller integer and 2 is subtracted from the larger integer, what is the product of the two resulting integers?

A. 63

B. 60

C. 56

D. 72

55) A sports store has a container of handballs: 7 blue, 10 red, 11 yellow, 8 white, and 4 greens. If one ball is picked from the container at random, what is the probability that it will be green?

A. $\dfrac{1}{4}$

B. $\dfrac{1}{10}$

C. $\dfrac{1}{9}$

D. $\dfrac{9}{10}$

56) $3 + (5n + 8) - (6n + 5)$

A. $6 - n$

B. $6 + n$

C. $16 - n$

D. $16 + n$

57) Jimmy must read 161 pages for school this weekend. It took him 20 minutes to read the first 14 pages. At this rate, how much additional time will it take him to finish the reading?

A. $1\dfrac{3}{7}$

B. $3\dfrac{5}{6}$

C. $3\dfrac{1}{2}$

D. $8\dfrac{1}{20}$

58) If the line m is parallel to the side BC of ABC, what is angle n?

    A. 115

    B. 65

    C. 25

    D. 15

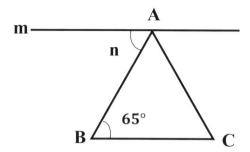

59) The cost of 1 pound of fruit is $2.70. How many pounds of food can be bought

    for $14.00?

    A. 0.52 pounds

    B. 5.1 pounds

    C. 51.9 pounds

    D. 5.2 pounds

60) Given that 12 cm on a map represents 9 km on the ground, calculate the distance

    in km between two points, which are 15 cm apart on the map.

    A. 7.2 km

    B. 11.25 km

    C. 36 km

    D. 20 km

61) What is the percent equivalent of 0.004?

    A. 40%

    B. 4%

    C. 0.40%

    D. 0.04%

62) When a number is subtracted from 90 and the result is divided by 7, the answer obtained is twice the original number. What is the number?

    A. 6

    B. 9

    C. 10

    D. 7

63) Tiffani's base salary last year was $54,000, not including her bonus. When she opened her HR profile, she saw that her total compensation added up to $63,000. This total included her bonus, as well as health benefits equivalent to 12% of her base salary. What percentage of Tiffani's base salary plus benefits was her bonus (Rounded to the nearest tenth)?

    A. 4.1

    B. 0.9

    C. 4.2

    D. 14.3

64) The operation is defined as $a @ b = a - 2ab$

The operation # is defined as $a\#b = 2a - b^2$

If $f(x) = -x^2 - 4$, what is the value of $(f(-1)@ f(2))\#f(3)$?

    A. -62

    B. -35

    C. -235

    D. 165

"End of HSPT Practice Test 6."

Answers and

Explanations

Answer Key

Now, it's time to review your results to see where you went wrong and what areas you need to improve!

HSPT Math Practice Test

Practice Test 1

1	C	23	D	45	B
2	D	24	C	46	D
3	B	25	B	47	A
4	A	26	C	48	B
5	B	27	C	49	D
6	B	28	A	50	B
7	A	29	D	51	A
8	B	30	B	52	C
9	A	31	A	53	C
10	B	32	D	54	B
11	C	33	A	55	A
12	B	34	D	56	C
13	B	35	C	57	C
14	B	36	B	58	A
15	C	37	D	59	D
16	A	38	B	60	C
17	C	39	C	61	C
18	D	40	D	62	C
19	A	41	C	63	B
20	B	42	B	64	D
21	B	43	A		
22	C	44	D		

Practice Test 2

1	C	23	C	45	C
2	B	24	D	46	A
3	D	25	A	47	B
4	A	26	C	48	C
5	C	27	D	49	D
6	D	28	B	50	B
7	A	29	A	51	C
8	A	30	D	52	B
9	C	31	A	53	A
10	B	32	C	54	A
11	D	33	C	55	B
12	C	34	B	56	A
13	C	35	D	57	C
14	D	36	D	58	B
15	A	37	C	59	D
16	C	38	A	60	B
17	D	39	B	61	C
18	C	40	D	62	A
19	B	41	B	63	C
20	C	42	D	64	B
21	A	43	C		
22	D	44	D		

HSPT Math Practice Test

Practice Test 3

1	C	23	D	45	B
2	D	24	C	46	D
3	B	25	B	47	A
4	A	26	C	48	B
5	B	27	C	49	D
6	B	28	A	50	B
7	A	29	D	51	A
8	B	30	B	52	C
9	A	31	A	53	C
10	B	32	D	54	B
11	C	33	A	55	A
12	B	34	D	56	C
13	B	35	C	57	C
14	B	36	B	58	A
15	C	37	D	59	D
16	A	38	B	60	C
17	C	39	C	61	C
18	D	40	D	62	C
19	A	41	C	63	B
20	B	42	B	64	D
21	B	43	A		
22	C	44	D		

Practice Test 4

1	C	23	C	45	C
2	B	24	D	46	A
3	D	25	A	47	B
4	A	26	C	48	C
5	C	27	D	49	D
6	D	28	B	50	B
7	A	29	A	51	C
8	A	30	D	52	B
9	C	31	A	53	A
10	B	32	C	54	A
11	D	33	C	55	B
12	C	34	B	56	A
13	C	35	D	57	C
14	D	36	D	58	B
15	A	37	C	59	D
16	C	38	A	60	B
17	D	39	B	61	C
18	C	40	D	62	A
19	B	41	B	63	C
20	C	42	D	64	B
21	A	43	C		
22	D	44	D		

HSPT Math Practice Test

Practice Test 5

1	C	23	D	45	B
2	D	24	C	46	D
3	B	25	B	47	A
4	A	26	C	48	B
5	B	27	C	49	D
6	B	28	A	50	B
7	A	29	D	51	A
8	B	30	B	52	C
9	A	31	A	53	C
10	B	32	D	54	B
11	C	33	A	55	A
12	B	34	D	56	C
13	B	35	C	57	C
14	B	36	B	58	A
15	C	37	D	59	D
16	A	38	B	60	C
17	C	39	C	61	C
18	D	40	D	62	C
19	A	41	C	63	B
20	B	42	B	64	D
21	B	43	A		
22	C	44	D		

Practice Test 6

1	C	23	C	45	C
2	B	24	D	46	A
3	D	25	A	47	B
4	A	26	C	48	C
5	C	27	D	49	D
6	D	28	B	50	B
7	A	29	A	51	C
8	A	30	D	52	B
9	C	31	A	53	A
10	B	32	C	54	A
11	D	33	C	55	B
12	C	34	B	56	A
13	C	35	D	57	C
14	D	36	D	58	B
15	A	37	C	59	D
16	C	38	A	60	B
17	D	39	B	61	C
18	C	40	D	62	A
19	B	41	B	63	C
20	C	42	D	64	B
21	A	43	C		
22	D	44	D		

HSPT Practice Test 1

Answers and Explanations

1) Answer: C

$\frac{-46}{5} = -9.2$ and $\frac{57}{7} = 8.1$, then the odd numbers are:

$(-9, -7, -5, -3, -1, 1, 3, 5, 7)$

2) Answer: D

The distance between two points always is positive. Use formula:

$AB = |b - a|$ or $|a - b| \rightarrow |-3 - 10|$ or $|10 - (-3)| = |10 + 3|$

3) Answer: B

Sum of the measures of the angles of a triangle is 180, if two angles are 60 then the third one is 60, then the triangle is equilateral triangle, and all side are equal.

4) Answer: A

All factors of 12 are: 1, 2, 3, 4, 6, 12, then sum of them is 28.

5) Answer: B

$\frac{1}{4} + \frac{2}{7} = \frac{7}{28} + \frac{8}{28} = \frac{15}{28}$

$1 - \frac{15}{28} = \frac{28}{28} - \frac{15}{28} = \frac{13}{28}$

6) Answer: B

Each next term after first term is found by multiplying the previous term by $\frac{1}{30}$,

then the choice B is correct.

7) Answer: A

Start to list factors of each number:

Factors of 14: 1, 2, 7, 14

Factors of 35: 1, 5, 7, 35

Factors of 30: 1, 2, 3, 5, 6, 10, 15, 30

The greatest common factor is 1.

8) Answer: B

9 more: $+9$

Ratio: $\div$; Ratio of a number to 6: $\frac{x}{6}$

8 less: -8 ; 8 less than the number: $x - 8$

$9 + \frac{x}{6} = x - 8$

9) Answer: A

Rewriting each fraction with common denominator or converting each fraction to decimal and order the decimal from least to greatest.

$\frac{5}{9} = 0.56$ $\frac{2}{5} = 0.4$ $\frac{1}{8} = 0.125$ $\frac{25}{28} = 0.89$ $\frac{12}{17} = 0.70$

10) Answer: B

calculating Elena's total earnings:

36 hours $\times$ \$6.50 an hour = \$234

Next, divide this total by her brother's hourly rate:

\$234 $\div$ \$9.75 = 24 hours

11) Answer: C

number of fiction books: x

number of nonfiction books: $x + 1,500$

Total number of books: $x + (x + 1,500)$

20% of the total number of books are fiction, therefore:

$20\%[x + (x + 1,500)] = x \rightarrow 0.2(2x + 1,500) = x$

$0.4x + 300 = x \ \rightarrow 300 = x - 0.4x \ \rightarrow 0.6x = 300$

$\rightarrow x = 500$ number of fictions

$x + 1,500 = 500 + 1,500 = 2,000$, the number of nonfiction books

$500 + 2,000 = 2,500$, the total number of books in the library

12) Answer: B

The scale is: 6 cm:1km, (6 cm on the map represents an actual distance of 1 km).

first necessary to rewrite the scale ratio in terms of units squared:

6^2cm square:1^2km square, which gives $36\ cm^2: 1\ km^2$

Then, $\frac{36\ cm^2}{1km^2} = \frac{90\ cm^2}{x\ km^2}$, (where x is the unknown actual area).

Every proportion you write should maintain consistency in the ratios described

(km^2 both occupy the denominator).

Cross-multiply and isolate to solve for the unknown area x:

$x.\frac{36\ cm^2}{1km^2} = 90\ cm^2 \rightarrow x = 90\ cm^2.\frac{1\ km^2}{36\ cm^2} \rightarrow x = 2.5\ km^2$

13) Answer: B

move decimal point in divisor so last digit is in the unit place (0.3 to 3)

move decimal point in dividend same number of places to the right,

(15.15 to 151.5)

divide $(1{,}515 \div 3){=}505$

insert a decimal point into the answer above the decimal point in the dividend

(50.5)

14) Answer: B

Circumference$= 2\pi r = 2 \times \pi \times 9 = 18\pi$

15) Answer: C

Be careful with the conversion factor (per hundred gallons; NOT per gallon).

$31{,}500 \times \frac{0.86}{100} = 270.9$

$270.9 + 5.30 = 276.2$

16) Answer: A

$\frac{(3x^4-6x^3)}{(x^3-2x^2)} = \frac{3x^3(x-2)}{x^2(x-2)} = 3x$

17) Answer: C

For odd index we can have negative radicand.

In the even index, negative radicand is undefined.

$\sqrt{-25}$ has a negative number under the even index, so it is non-real.

Negative numbers don't have real square roots, because negative and positive integer squared is either positive or 0.

18) Answer: D

$4f(3a) = 864 \rightarrow$ (divide by 4): $f(3a) = 216$

(subtitute 3a) $6(3a)^2 = 216 \rightarrow$ (divide by 6): $(3a)^2 = 36 \rightarrow 9a^2 = 36 \rightarrow$

$a^2 = 4 \rightarrow a = 2$

19) Answer: A

3 hours and 25 minutes is 3.25 hour.

$R \times T = D \rightarrow 140 \times 3.25 = D \rightarrow D = 455$ miles

20) Answer: B

$5x - 8 \leq 12x + 6 \rightarrow Add\ 8: 5x - 8 + 8 \leq 12x + 6 + 8 \rightarrow$

$subtract\ 12x: 5x - 12x \leq 12x - 12x + 14 \rightarrow -7x \leq 14 \rightarrow x \geq -2$

21) Answer: B

Use formula to raise a number: $(x^a)^b = x^{ab}$

$2^8 = (2^2)^4 = 4^4$

22) Answer: C

Simple interest rate: I = prt (I = interest, p = principal, r = rate, t = time)

$I = 4,200 \times 0.038 \times 5 = 798$

23) Answer: D

A straight angle is an angle measured exactly $180°$

$$61° + 42° = 103°$$

$$180° - 103° = 77°$$

24) Answer: C

$$\frac{15x^7y^4z^{-4}}{6\,x^3y^8z^2} = \frac{15}{6} \times \frac{x^7}{x^3} \times \frac{y^4}{y^8} \times \frac{z^{-4}}{z^2} = \frac{5}{2} \times x^4 \times \frac{1}{y^4} \times \frac{1}{z^6} = \frac{5x^4}{2\,y^4z^6}$$

25) Answer: B

$$m = \frac{y_2 - y_1}{x_2 - x_1} = \frac{3 - (-2)}{4 - 1} = \frac{5}{3}$$

$$y - y_1 = m(x - x_1) \rightarrow y - (-3) = \frac{5}{3}(x - 4)$$

$$y + 3 = \frac{5}{3}(x - 4) \rightarrow 3(y + 3) = 5(x - 4) \rightarrow 3y + 9 = 5x - 20$$

$$3y - 5x = -20 - 9 \rightarrow 3y - 5x = -29$$

26) Answer: C

$$\frac{x^2 + 12}{y - 2} = \frac{(-3)^2 + 12}{5 - 2} = \frac{21}{3} = 7$$

27) Answer: C

Ethan paid \$4.2 for three hours and \$1.25 for each of three half-hour period after that.

$$3 \times 1.25 = 3.75$$

$$4.2 + 3.75 = 7.95$$

28) Answer: A

Cross multiply and isolate x: $\frac{c - d}{dx} = \frac{3}{5} \rightarrow 5(c - d) = 3dx \rightarrow x = \frac{5(c - d)}{3d}$

$$x = \frac{5}{3}\left(\frac{c}{d} - \frac{d}{d}\right) = \frac{5}{3}\left(\frac{c}{d} - 1\right)$$

29) Answer: D

$$4x^4 - x^2 = x^2(4x^2 - 1) = x^2(2x - 1)(2x + 1)$$

30) Answer: B

Factoring: $(x - 7)(x - 9) = 0 \rightarrow \begin{cases} x - 7 = 0 \rightarrow x = 7 \\ x - 9 = 0 \rightarrow x = 9 \end{cases}$

31) Answer: A

Two points are $(0,1)$ and $(8,3)$; $m = \frac{y_2 - y_1}{x_2 - x_1} = \frac{3 - 1}{8 - 0} = \frac{2}{8} = \frac{1}{4}$

$$y - y_1 = m(x - x_1) \rightarrow y - 1 = \frac{1}{4}(x - 0)$$

$$y - 1 = \frac{1}{4}x \rightarrow y = \frac{1}{4}x + 1$$

32) Answer: D

$$\begin{cases} 2 \times (-4x + 5y = -4) \\ 5 \times (3x - 2y = 3) \end{cases} \rightarrow \begin{cases} -8x + 10y = -8 \\ 15x - 10y = 15 \end{cases} \rightarrow \text{add two equations:}$$

$$7x = 7 \rightarrow x = 1$$

33) Answer: A

Triangle third side rule: length of the one side of a triangle is less than the sum of the lengths of the other two sides and greater than the positive difference of the lengths of the other two sides.

the third side is less than 7+4=11 and greater than 7−4=3

34) Answer: D

Mean = $(121 + 129 + 136 + 149 + 167 + 174) \div 6 = 876 \div 6 = 146$

Only 151 can increase the mean.

35) Answer: C

The mode is the value which occurs with the greatest frequency. Oregon and Ohio are greatest and the same frequency (3 times).

36) Answer: B

convert the given distance, 9 km, into centimeters, (units on the map)

9 km = 9,000 m = 900,000 cm; divide by the ratio 1:60,000.

$$\frac{900,000}{60,000} = 15 \text{ cm}$$

37) Answer: D

Area of square is: $a^2 = (\sqrt{11})^2 = 11$

38) Answer: B

$$3x^3 y^2 (2x^2 y^2)^5 = 3x^3 y^2 (32x^{10} y^{10}) = 96x^{13} y^{12}$$

39) Answer: C

Change percent to decimal: $15\% = 0.15$

$0.15 \times 180 = 27$

40) Answer: D

Using the formula for mean:

$$\text{Mean} = \frac{sum\ of\ the\ several\ given\ values}{number\ of\ value\ given}$$

$$= \frac{x+(x-6)+(x-6)}{3} = \frac{3x-12}{3} = \frac{3(x-4)}{3} = x - 4$$

41) Answer: C

a value that is inversely proportional to another value: $a = \frac{k}{3b-8}$ (where k is a constant of proportionality)

substitute a and b: $12 = \frac{k}{3(6)-8} \to k = 12(10) = 120$

$$a = \frac{120}{3b-8}$$

42) Answer: B

Baseballs and basketballs are spherical. The volume of sphere: $v = \frac{4}{3}\pi r^3$

$$972\pi = \frac{4}{3}\pi r^3 \to 972 = \frac{4}{3}r^3 \to 2{,}916 = 4r^3 \to r^3 = 729 \to r = 9$$

$$d = 2r \to d = 2 \times 9 = 18$$

43) Answer: A

Use percent formula: $\text{Part} = \frac{percent \times whole}{100}$

$$168 = \frac{percent \times 120}{100} \Rightarrow \frac{168}{1} = \frac{percent \times 120}{100}, \text{ cross multiply.}$$

$16{,}800 = \text{percent} \times 120$, divide both sides by 120. $\to$ percent= 140

44) Answer: D

The sample shows that 4 out of 300 phones will be faulty. Consequently, a proportion can be set up.

$$\frac{4}{300} = \frac{P}{15{,}000} \text{ (P: Faulty Phone)} \to P = \frac{4 \times 15{,}000}{300} = 200$$

45) Answer: B

We can Write an equation to solve the problem.

Emma Books =Mia books +3 →Mia book = Emma – 3 = b – 3

Emma + Mia=25

$b + b - 3 = 25 \rightarrow 2b - 3 = 25 \rightarrow 2b = 25 + 3 \rightarrow b = 14$

46) Answer: D

Probability = $\dfrac{number\ of\ desired\ outcomes}{number\ of\ total\ outcomes} = \dfrac{7}{4+3+7} = \dfrac{7}{14} = \dfrac{1}{2} = 0.5$

47) Answer: A

Surface Area of a cylinder = $2\pi r\ (r + h)$,

The radius of the cylinder is 3 inches, and its height are 7 inches. π is 3.14. Then:

Surface Area of a cylinder = 2 (3.14) (3) (3 + 7) = 188.4 inches

48) Answer: B

use the Pythagorean theorem to find the value of unknown side.

$a^2 + b^2 = c^2 \rightarrow c^2 = 21^2 + 28^2 \rightarrow a^2 = 441 + 784 = 1{,}225 \rightarrow c = 35$

49) Answer: D

A line perpendicular to a line with slope m has a slope of $-\dfrac{1}{m}$.

So, the slope of the line perpendicular to the given line is $-\dfrac{1}{\frac{a}{b}} = -\dfrac{b}{a}$.

50) Answer: B.

For a value of x to satisfy the provided equation, it must be a solution. The equation provided should be recognized as a quadratic equation, which can be factored using many methods.

2 can be divided out of both sides: $2x^2 - 16x + 32 = 0$,

$$x^2 - 8x + 16 = 0$$

In order to further simplify this expression and solve for x, we must factor. We are looking for 2 numbers that, when multiplied together, yield +16, and when added together yield −8.

+16 factors: $\pm(1 \times 16), \pm(4 \times 4)$

$$(x - 4)(x - 4) = 0$$

$$x - 4 = 0 \rightarrow x = 4$$

So, x must equal $+4$. This answer can be confirmed by substituting $+4$ into the original equation: $4^2 - 8(4) + 16 = 16 - 32 + 16 = 0$

51) Answer: A

subtracting 7 from both sides: $-\frac{(3x-9)}{5} \geq 3$

Multiply both sides by -5: $(3x - 9) \leq -15$

This operation clears the negative sign and the denominator of 5 from the left side. Add 9 to both sides and divide by 3 to isolate x:

$$3x \leq -6 \rightarrow x \leq -2$$

52) Answer: C.

Recall that dividing fractions is the same as multiplying the first fraction by its reciprocal (numerator and denominator are switched).

First rewrite the expression as a multiplication problem, switching numerator with denominator in the second fraction. Then, factor and simplify, where possible:

$$\frac{(x^2+7x+12)}{(2x^2-4x+2)} \times \frac{(x^2-6x+5)}{(x^2-x-20)} = \frac{(x+3)(x+4)}{2(x-1)^2} \times \frac{(x-1)(x-5)}{(x-5)(x+4)} = \frac{x+3}{2(x-1)} = \frac{x+3}{2x-2}$$

53) Answer: C

If 22% of the total number of customers is female, then $100\% - 22\% = 78\%$ of the customers are male. Calculate 78% of the total.

$0.78 \times 800 = 624$.

54) Answer: B

First, add the numbers given in the proportion to get a denominator: $7 + 4 = 11$.

Then, the two parts can be represented as $\frac{7}{11}$ and $\frac{4}{11}$.

The smaller share is $\frac{4}{11}$ of 72.3 kg: $\frac{4}{11} \times 72.3 \ kg = 26.29$

55) Answer: A

Since this is subtraction of 2 fractions with different denominators, their least common denominator is: $(x - 1)(2x + 3)$

$$\frac{3}{(x-1)} - \frac{4}{(2x+3)} = \frac{3(2x+3)-4(x-1)}{(x-1)(2x+3)} = \frac{6x+9-4x+4}{(x-1)(2x+3)} = \frac{2x+13}{(x-1)(2x+3)}$$

56) Answer: C

State the problem in a mathematical equation:

$$3x = 7x - 16 \rightarrow 3x - 7x = -16 \rightarrow -4x = -16 \rightarrow x = \frac{-16}{-4} = 4$$

$$7x - 16 = 7(4) - 16 = 12$$

57) Answer: C

$4h = 3p + 4$:

$$p = 4 \rightarrow 4h = 3(4) + 4 = 16 \rightarrow 4h = 16 \rightarrow h = 4$$

$$p = 8 \rightarrow 4h = 3(8) + 4 = 28 \rightarrow 4h = 28 \rightarrow h = 7$$

$$p = 12 \rightarrow 4h = 3(12) + 4 = 40 \rightarrow 4h = 40 \rightarrow h = 10$$

possible values of h: $\{4, 7, 10\}$

58) Answer: A

There are 6 digits in the repeating decimal (076923), so 7 would be the second, eighth, fourteenth digit and so on.

To find the 440st digit, divide 440 by 6.

$440 \div 6 = 73$ R2

Since the remainder is 2, that means the 440st digit is the same as the 2nd digit, which is 7.

59) Answer: D

Percentage of a fraction and another fraction.

$$\frac{1}{6} = \left(\frac{x}{100}\right)\frac{2}{9} \Rightarrow \frac{1}{6} = \frac{2x}{900} \Rightarrow 900 = 12x \Rightarrow x = 75$$

60) Answer: C

Each number is the sum of the previous and the number 2 places to the left.

Which is mean: $18 + 8 = 26$

61) Answer: C

Use the distributive property to open the parentheses and combine like terms where possible.

use FOIL method: First terms, Outside terms, Inside terms, and Last terms.

$(2y - 3x)(4x - y) = ((2y)(4x)) + ((2y)(-y)) + ((-3x)(4x)) + ((-3x)(-y)) = 8xy - 2y^2 - 12x^2 + 3xy = -12x^2 + 11xy - 2y^2$

62) Answer: C

To solve for y, subtracting 2.75 from both sides of the equation:

$-0.4y = -0.37 - 2.75 \rightarrow -0.4y = -3.12$

Divide both sides by -0.4: $y = 7.8$

63) Answer: B

To find the area Joey needs to cover, $6 \times 12 = 72$ square feet.

Convert inches to feet: 18 inches = 1.5 feet.

Each board measures 1.5×6 feet, which equals coverage of 9 square foot.

He will need 8 of these to cover 72 square feet ($72 \div 9 = 8$).

64) Answer: D

volume of the cube: $V = S^3$

S is Side length: $120 \, cm = \frac{120}{100} = 1.2 \, m$

$V = (1.2)^3 = 1.728 \, m^3$

HSPT Practice Test 2

Answers and Explanations

1) Answer: C

The smallest prime number is 2, and the largest even negative integer is -2.

$2 + 6(-2) = 2 - 12 = -10$.

2) Answer: B

The difference between his income and his cost is monthly saving.

January: $\$2,780 - \$1,002 = \$1,778$

February: $\$2,895 - \$975 = \$1,920$

March: $\$2,990 - \$1,012 = \$1,978$

3) Answer: D

State the problem in a mathematical sentence:

$a + 38 = 272 - 5a$

$a + 5a = 272 - 38$

$6a = 234 \rightarrow a = 39$

4) Answer: A

$$7\frac{5}{32} - 4\frac{1}{4} + 3\frac{3}{8} = (7 - 4 + 3)\frac{5}{32} - \frac{8}{32} + \frac{12}{32} = 6(\frac{-3}{32} + \frac{12}{32}) = 6(\frac{12-3}{32}) = 6\frac{9}{32}$$

5) Answer: C

$5^2 + 5 + 5^0 = 25 + 5 + 1 = 31$

6) Answer: D

$\frac{133}{190} = \frac{133}{19} \times \frac{1}{10} = 7 \times \frac{1}{10} = 0.7$

7) Answer: A

Use the formula for Percent of Change:

$$\frac{\text{New Value} - \text{Old Value}}{\text{Old Value}} \times 100\% = \frac{42.40 - 40}{40} \times 100\% = \frac{2.40}{40} \times 100\% = 6\%$$

8) Answer: A

$$|3x - 6| = 9 \rightarrow \begin{cases} 3x - 6 = 9 \rightarrow 3x = 15 \rightarrow x = 5 \\ 3x - 6 = -9 \rightarrow 3x = -3 \rightarrow x = -1 \end{cases}$$

9) Answer: C

Multiply equation (2) by 4. Add two equations [(1) +4(2)]:

$$\begin{cases} x - 4y = 6 \\ 12x + 4y = 20 \end{cases} \rightarrow 13x = 26 \rightarrow x = 2$$

Substitute $x = 2$ into equation (1): $2 - 4y = 6 \rightarrow -4y = 4 \rightarrow y = -1$

10) Answer: B

4 hours equals 240 minutes. The train passes 3 stations every 20 minutes: $\frac{3}{20}$

$$\frac{3}{20} = \frac{x}{240} \rightarrow x = \frac{240 \times 3}{20} = 36 \text{ stations}$$

11) Answer: D

Difference in percent: $12\% - 10\% = 2\%$

$2\% \times 170 = 0.02 \times 170 = 3.40$

12) Answer: C.

$C = \pi d = 2\pi r = 2\pi \times 29 = 58\,\pi$

13) Answer: C

$V = l \times w \times h = 23 \times 10 \times 13 = 2{,}990\ in^3$

14) Answer: D

$$\sqrt[3]{3^{-9}} = \sqrt[3]{\frac{1}{3^9}} = \frac{\sqrt[3]{1}}{\sqrt[3]{3^9}} = \frac{1}{3^{\left(\frac{9}{3}\right)}} = \frac{1}{3^3} = 3^{-3} = \frac{1}{27}$$

15) Answer: A

There are no values of the variable that make the equation true.

16) Answer: C

Volume of cylinder: $V = \pi r^2 h = \pi \times 6^2 \times 10 = 360\pi$

Volume of cone: $V = \frac{1}{3}\pi r^2 h = \frac{1}{3}\pi \times 6^2 \times 4 = 48\pi$

$360\pi + 48\pi = 408\pi.$

17) Answer: D

$7.59 \times 10^{-3} = 0.00759$

18) Answer: C

$x + 49 + 46 + 39 = 180 \rightarrow x + 134 = 180 \rightarrow x = 46$

19) Answer: B

use the Pythagorean theorem to find the value of unknown side.

$a^2 + b^2 = c^2 \rightarrow 30^2 = a^2 + 18^2 \rightarrow a^2 = 900 - 324 = 576 \rightarrow a = 24$

20) Answer: C

Use percent formula: $\text{Part} = \frac{\text{percent} \times \text{whole}}{100} \rightarrow \text{Part} = \frac{15 \times 160}{100} = 24$

Last price: $160 + 24 = \$184$

21) Answer: A

Area of trapezoid: $\frac{(a+b)}{2} \times h \rightarrow A = \frac{(10+13)}{2} \times 8 = 92$

Area of triangle: $\frac{b \times h}{2} \rightarrow A = \frac{6 \times 8}{2} = 24$

Area of shaded region: $92 - 24 = 68$

22) Answer: D

$xy - 9x = 42 \rightarrow x(y - 9) = 42$

$7x = 42 \rightarrow x = 6$

23) Answer: C

Multiply both sides by 5: $5 \times \left(\frac{x}{5}\right) = 5 \times (x - 8) \rightarrow x = 5x - 40$

Subtract both side by x and add 40 to both sides: $40 + x - x = 5x - x - 40 +$

$40 \rightarrow 4x = 40 \rightarrow x = 10$

24) Answer: D

$\begin{cases} 5 \times (-7x + 3y = 8) \\ -3 \times (-6x + 5y = 2) \end{cases} \rightarrow \begin{cases} -35x + 15y = 40 \\ 18x - 15y = -6 \end{cases} \rightarrow$ add two equations:

$-17x = 34 \rightarrow x = -2$

25) Answer: A

There are 4 parts labeled "H" out of a total of 8 equal parts.

The probability of not spinning at "H" is 4 out of 8.

26) Answer: C

The best estimate of the product of 42 and 4.06 to the nearest whole number.

Since 42 is already a whole number and 4.06 is closer to 4 than 5. Option C is the correct answer.

27) Answer: D

Fuel consumption rate $= \frac{9}{60} = 0.15$ liter per mile

Cost: $1,400 \times 0.15 \times 1.20 = 252$

28) Answer: B

Point $1(x_A, y_A) = (-3, -5)$; Point $2(x_B, y_B) = (1, -2)$

Distance between two points $= \sqrt{(x_B - x_A)^2 + (y_B - y_A)^2}$

$$\rightarrow d = \sqrt{\left(1 - (-3)\right)^2 + \left(-2 - (-5)\right)^2} = \sqrt{4^2 + 3^2} = \sqrt{16 + 9}$$

$$\rightarrow d = \sqrt{25} = 5$$

29) Answer: A

Ordered values: 98, 156, 188, 215, 230, 389, 401.

The 4th number is median.

30) Answer: D

$\sqrt{5x - 6} = 7 \rightarrow 5x - 6 = 49 \rightarrow 5x = 55 \rightarrow x = 11$

31) Answer: A

Get the equation into slop intercept form:

$y = mx + b$ where m is slope and b is y-intercept.

$x = 3y - 9$; Add 9 to both sides $\rightarrow x + 9 = 3y$; Dividing by 3: $\rightarrow y = \frac{1}{3}x + 3$

Thus, the y-intercept is 3.

32) Answer: C

$2^{3x} = 64 \rightarrow (2^3)^x = 64 \rightarrow 8^x = 8^2 \rightarrow x = 2$

33) Answer: C

$32: 2 \times 2 \times 2 \times 2 \times 2$

$48: 2 \times 2 \times 2 \times 2 \times 3$

LCM $(48, 32) = 2 \times 2 \times 2 \times 2 \times 2 \times 3 = 96$

34) Answer: B

Surface area $(SA): 6a^2 \rightarrow 150 = 6a^2 \rightarrow a^2 = 25 \rightarrow a = 5$ cm

Volume $(v): a^3 \rightarrow v = 5^3 = 125$ cm^3

35) Answer: D

Write the equation into standard form: $x^2 + 4x = 32 \rightarrow x^2 + 4x - 32 = 0$

Factor this expression: $(x - 4)(x + 8) = 0 \rightarrow x = 4 \ or, x = -8 \rightarrow x^2 = \begin{cases} 16 \\ 64 \end{cases}$

36) Answer: D

The minimum amount of water: $8 \times \frac{7}{8} = 7; \ 7 \div 4 = 1.75$

The maximum amount of water: $8 \times \frac{7}{8} = 7$

Amount of water in all pitchers: $1.75 < w < 7$

37) Answer: C

The range is: highest value – lowest value.

R $= 51 - 16 = 35$

38) Answer: A

d $= 2r \rightarrow r = \frac{d}{2} = \frac{22}{2} = 11$

Area of circle (A): $\pi r^2 = \pi \times 11^2 = 379.94 \cong 379.9$

39) Answer: B

Factor the expression: $\frac{3x^2 - 14x - 5}{9(x^2 - \frac{1}{9})} = \frac{(x-5)(3x+1)}{9x^2 - 1} = \frac{(x-5)(3x+1)}{(3x-1)(3x+1)} = \frac{x-5}{3x-1}$

40) Answer: D

$$\left(\frac{1}{2}\right)^{-5} = \frac{1}{2^{-5}} = 2^5 = 32$$

41) Answer: B

$$\frac{(6x^{-4}y^2)^2}{252y^{-3}z^0} = \frac{36x^{-8}y^4}{252y^{-3}z^0} = \frac{y^7}{7x^8}$$

42) Answer: D

$$\text{Rate: } \frac{\$1}{1Kg} = \frac{100\cancel{c}}{1,000g} \rightarrow 1\,^{\$}/_{kg} = 0.1\,^{\cancel{c}}/_{g}$$

The price is: $20 \times 0.1 = 2$cent per kilogram.

43) Answer: C

$4P = 8 \rightarrow P = 2$ The price of 2007 is one-fourth of 2012 ($8 \div 4 = 2$)

44) Answer: D

First equation: $3y + 4 = 18x + 7 \rightarrow 3y = 18x + 3 \rightarrow y = 6x + 1 \rightarrow m_1 = 6$

Second question: $6y - 2 = x + 3 \rightarrow 6y = x + 5 \rightarrow y = \frac{1}{6}x + \frac{5}{6} \rightarrow m_2 = \frac{1}{6}$

$m_1 = 6$ and $m_2 = \frac{1}{6}$, they aren't equal slopes or negative reciprocals.

45) Answer: C

$$\text{Area} = 7\frac{1}{3} \times 6\frac{3}{4} = \frac{22}{3} \times \frac{27}{4} = \frac{594}{12} = \frac{99}{2} \text{ square feet.}$$

$$\text{One-fourth} = \frac{99}{2} \div 3 = \frac{99}{2} \times \frac{1}{3} = \frac{99}{6} = \frac{33}{2} = 16.5$$

46) Answer: A

Two points are $(6, 2)$ and $(-6, -4) \rightarrow m = \frac{y_2 - y_1}{x_2 - x_1} = \frac{-4 - 2}{-6 - 6} = \frac{-6}{-12} = \frac{1}{2}$

47) Answer: B

$$V = \left(\frac{base \times height}{2}\right) \times \text{height of prism} \rightarrow V = \left(\frac{8 \times 17}{2}\right) \times 6 = 408$$

48) Answer: C

f(a) $= 3a - 6$ and f(a) $= -15$: $3a - 6 = -15$ so that $3a = -9$ and a $= -3$.

f(b) $= 3b - 6$ and f(b) $= 6$: $3b - 6 = 6$ so that $3b = 12$ and b $= 4$

Finally, f(a + b) = f(−3 + 4) = f(1)

   f(1) = 3(1) − 6 = −3.

49) Answer: D

The ratio of $x:y$ is equivalent to x divided by y, or $\frac{x}{y}$.

Equation: $10x = 4y$

Dividing both sides by 10: $x = \frac{4y}{10}$

Dividing both sides by y: $\frac{x}{y} = \frac{4}{10} = \frac{2}{5}$

Then, $x:y$ is $2:5$

50) Answer: B

Method 1:

The formula for measurement of each angle of a regular polygon:

$x = \frac{180(n-2)}{n}$, (x is the measurement of the interior angle; n is the number of sides)

Substituting the given information:

$\frac{180(n-2)}{n} = 162 \rightarrow 180n - 360 = 162n \rightarrow 180n - 162n = 360$

$\rightarrow 18n = 360 \rightarrow n = 20$; The polygon has 20 angles and 20 sides.

Method 2:

The sum of exterior angles of any polygon is always equal to 360 degrees.

Exterior angle(degrees) $\times n = 360$; (n, is the number of angles (sides)).

Exterior angle = 180 – interior angle

The exterior angle = 180 – 162 = 18 degrees

Then, $18n = 360 \rightarrow n = 360 \div 18 = 20$;

The polygon has 20 angles and 20 sides.

51) Answer: C

Age of Jim: x and the age of Jim 3 years ago: $x - 3$

The age of Frank: $7x$ and the age of Frank 3 years ago: $7x - 3$

$(x - 3)(7x - 3) = 25$

$7x^2 - 3x - 21x + 9 = 25 \rightarrow 7x^2 - 24x - 16 = 0$

$(7x + 4)(x - 4) = 0$

$7x + 4 = 0$ will yield a negative value for x, so this is not possible solution.

$x - 4 = 0 \rightarrow x = 4 \rightarrow$The age of Frank: $7x = 7(4) = 28$.

52) Answer: B

$\frac{d}{3} = \frac{12}{d}$ Cross-multiply: $d \times d = 3 \times 12 \rightarrow d^2 = 36$

Then, find the square root of both sides:

The actual square root of d^2 is $\pm d$ and the actual square root of 36 is ± 6, so:

$d = \pm 6$

Of the answer choices for this question, -6 is the best choice since it is the only

one that is true about the equation.

53) Answer: A

Let f be the points earned by FT, r be the points scored by RT, and g be the points

scored by GT.

f = 30% of $180 = 0.30 \times 180 = 54$ points

$180 = f + r + g \rightarrow 180 = 54 + 5g + g \rightarrow 180 - 54 = 6g$

$\rightarrow 6g = 126 \rightarrow g = 21; r = 5g \rightarrow r = 5(21) = 105$ points

54) Answer: A

If x is the smaller consecutive integer, then $x + 1$ is the larger consecutive

integer. Use their sum (-19) to find x:

$$x + (x + 1) = -19 \rightarrow 2x + 1 = -19 \rightarrow 2x = -20 \rightarrow x = -10$$

The two consecutive integers are -10 and -9.

three is added to the smaller integer: $-10 + 3 = -7$

and 1 is subtracted from the larger integer: $-9 - 1 = -10$

Find the product: $(-7)(-10) = 70$

55) Answer: B

The total number of handballs in the container is: $12 + 16 + 5 + 9 + 18 = 60$

Since there are 5 yellow handballs, the probability of selecting a green handball is

$\frac{5}{60} = \frac{1}{12}$

56) Answer: A

$4 + (7n + 9) - (8n + 3) = 4 + 7n + 9 - 8n - 3 = 10 - n$

57) Answer: C

Jimmy has 122 pages left to read $(134 - 12)$. $\frac{12}{30} = \frac{24}{60}$

He read at a rate of 24 pages per 1 hour. Then, divide the total number of pages

remaining (122) by the number of pages he can read per hour (24):

$\frac{122}{24} = 5\frac{1}{12}$

58) Answer: B

Two parallel lines (m & side BC) intersected by side AB.

$n = 70°$ (Interior angles)

59) Answer: D

Let x represent the number of pounds that can be bought for $15.00.

$\frac{1}{3.10} = \frac{x}{15}$

Cross multiply and solve the equation: $3.10x = 15 \rightarrow x = \frac{15}{3.10} = 4.8$

60) Answer: B

Let x represent the distance you are trying to find (in km).

The quickest way to solve for x is to create a proportion with the quantities

you do know. $\frac{km \; on \; ground}{cm \; on \; map}$; Substitute the numbers you know: $\frac{5}{14} = \frac{x}{21}$

Cross-multiply to get this equation and solve: $5 \times 21 = 14x \rightarrow x = \frac{105}{14} = 7.5$

61) Answer: C

To write a percent, move the decimal point two places to the right and follow the resulting number with the % sign. Or adding the % sign after multiplying the decimal number and 100: $0.009 \times 100 = 0.9\% = 0.90\%$

62) Answer: A

$\frac{(65-x)}{4} = 3x \rightarrow 65 - x = 4(3x) \rightarrow 65 = 12x + x \rightarrow x = \frac{65}{13} = 5$

63) Answer: C

Base salary: $45,000.

Health benefits: $45,000 \times 18\% = \$45,000 \times 0.18 = \$8,100$.

Her base salary, plus benefits: $45,000 + $8,100 = $53,100.

Since her total compensation: $57,000; Bonus: $57,000 – $53,100 = $3,900.

Calculate the percent of her bonus: $\frac{3,900}{53,100} = \frac{x}{100} \rightarrow x = \frac{390,000}{53,100} = 7.3$

64) Answer: B

Note: "@" and "#" are two "operations", and they are defined in the first two lines of the question.

Begin by evaluating $f(-2)$ and $f(3)$, Then, substitute $f(-2)$ and $f(3)$ into the first operation and substitute the appropriate values into the second operation.

$f(-2) = -(-2)^2 + 5 = -4 + 5 = 1$

$f(3) = -(3)^2 + 5 = -9 + 5 = -4$

$a @ b = a - 3ab$:

$(f(-2)@ f(3)) = (1)@(-4) = (1) - 3(1)(-4) = 1 + 12 = 13$

$a\#b = a - 2b^2$:

$f(1) = -(1)^2 + 5 = 4$

$(f(-2)@ f(3))\#f(1) = (13)\#f(1) = (13)\#(4) = 13 - 2(4)^2 = 13 - 2(16) = 13 - 32 = -19$

HSPT Practice Test 3
Answers and Explanations

1) Answer: C

$\frac{-69}{6} = -11.5$ and $\frac{19}{5} = 3.8$, then the odd numbers are:

$(-11, -9, -7, -5, -3, -1, 1, 3)$

2) Answer: D

The distance between two points always is positive. Use formula:

$AB = |b - a|$ or $|a - b| \rightarrow |-4 - 14|$ or $|14 - (-4)| = |14 + 4|$

3) Answer: B

Sum of the measures of the angles of a triangle is 180, if two angles are 60 then the third one is 60, then the triangle is equilateral triangle, and all side are equal.

4) Answer: A

All factors of 21 are: 1, 3, 7, 21, then sum of them is 32.

5) Answer: B

$\frac{1}{5} + \frac{3}{8} = \frac{8}{40} + \frac{15}{40} = \frac{23}{40}$

$1 - \frac{23}{40} = \frac{40}{40} - \frac{23}{40} = \frac{17}{40}$

6) Answer: B

Each next term after first term is found by multiplying the previous term by $\frac{1}{20}$, then the choice B is correct.

7) Answer: A

Start to list factors of each number:

Factors of 20: 1, 2, 4, 5, 10, 20

Factors of 28: 1, 2, 4, 7, 14, 28

Factors of 42: 1, 2, 3, 6, 7, 14, 21, 42

The greatest common factor is 2.

8) Answer: B

10 more: $+10$

Ratio: $\div$; Ratio of a number to 4: $\frac{x}{4}$

7 less: -7 ; 7 less than the number: $x - 7$

$10 + \frac{x}{4} = x - 7$

9) Answer: A

Rewriting each fraction with common denominator or converting each fraction to decimal and order the decimal from least to greatest.

$\frac{3}{8} = 0.375$ $\frac{4}{7} = 0.57$ $\frac{1}{5} = 0.2$ $\frac{23}{25} = 0.92$ $\frac{14}{19} = 0.73$

10) Answer: B

calculating Elena's total earnings:

33 hours $\times$ \$7.00 an hour $=$ \$231

Next, divide this total by her brother's hourly rate:

\$231 $\div$ \$8.25 $=$ 28 hours

11) Answer: C

number of fiction books: x ; number of nonfiction books: $x + 1,200$

Total number of books: $x + (x + 1,200)$

30% of the total number of books are fiction, therefore:

$30\%[x + (x + 1,200)] = x \rightarrow 0.3(2x + 1,200) = x$

$0.6x + 360 = x \rightarrow 360 = x - 0.6x \rightarrow 0.4x = 360$

$\rightarrow x = 900$ number of fictions

$x + 1,200 = 900 + 1,200 = 2,100$, the number of nonfiction books

$900 + 2,100 = 3,000$, the total number of books in the library

12) Answer: B

The scale is: 5 cm:1km, (5 cm on the map represents an actual distance of 1 km).

first necessary to rewrite the scale ratio in terms of units squared:

5^2cm square:1^2km square, which gives $25 \ cm^2 : 1 \ km^2$

Then, $\frac{25 \ cm^2}{1 km^2} = \frac{85 \ cm^2}{x \ km^2}$, (where x is the unknown actual area).

Every proportion you write should maintain consistency in the ratios described (km^2 both occupy the denominator).

Cross-multiply and isolate to solve for the unknown area x:

$$x. \frac{25 \ cm^2}{1 km^2} = 85 \ cm^2 \rightarrow x = 85 \ cm^2 . \frac{1 \ km^2}{25 \ cm^2} \rightarrow x = 3.4 \ km^2$$

13) Answer: B

move decimal point in divisor so last digit is in the unit place (0.9 to 9)

move decimal point in dividend same number of places to the right,

(45.45 to 454.5); divide (4,545 ÷ 9)=505

insert a decimal point into the answer above the decimal point in the dividend

(50.5)

14) Answer: B

Circumference= $2\pi r = 2 \times \pi \times 11 = 22\pi$

15) Answer: C

Be careful with the conversion factor (per hundred gallons; NOT per gallon).

$28,500 \times \frac{0.72}{100} = 205.2; \ 205.2 + 4.40 = 209.6$

16) Answer: A

$\frac{(2x^5+6x^4)}{(x^4+3x^2)} = \frac{2x^4(x+3)}{x^3(x+3)} = 2x$

17) Answer: C

For odd index we can have negative radicand.

In the even index, negative radicand is undefined.

$\sqrt{-49}$ has a negative number under the even index, so it is non-real.

Negative numbers don't have real square roots, because negative and positive integer squared is either positive or 0.

18) Answer: D

$5f(2a) = 180 \rightarrow$ (divide by 5): $f(2a) = 36$

(subtitute 2a) $3(2a)^2 = 108 \rightarrow$ (divide by3): $(2a)^2 = 36 \rightarrow 4a^2 = 36 \rightarrow$

$a^2 = 9 \rightarrow a = 3$

19) Answer: A

4 hours and 45 minutes is 4.45 hour.

$R \times T = D \rightarrow 160 \times 4.45 = D \rightarrow D = 712$ miles

20) Answer: B

$9x - 7 \leq 15x + 11 \rightarrow Add\ 7: 9x - 7 + 7 \leq 15x + 7 + 11 \rightarrow$

$subtract\ 15x: 9x - 15x \leq 15x - 15x + 18 \rightarrow -6x \leq 18 \rightarrow x \geq -3$

21) Answer: B

Use formula to raise a number: $(x^a)^b = x^{ab} \rightarrow 3^6 = (3^2)^3 = 9^3$

22) Answer: C

Simple interest rate: I = prt (I = interest, p = principal, r = rate, t = time)

$I = 3,600 \times 0.045 \times 2 = 324$

23) Answer: D

A straight angle is an angle measured exactly $180°$

$72° + 34° = 106°; 180° - 106° = 74°$

24) Answer: C

$\frac{21x^9y^2z^{-3}}{14\ x^5y^6z^3} = \frac{21}{14} \times \frac{x^9}{x^5} \times \frac{y^4}{y^8} \times \frac{z^{-3}}{z^3} = \frac{3}{2} \times x^4 \times \frac{1}{y^4} \times \frac{1}{z^6} = \frac{3x^4}{2\ y^4z^6}$

25) Answer: B

$m = \frac{y_2 - y_1}{x_2 - x_1} = \frac{1-(-4)}{5-2} = \frac{5}{3}$

$y - y_1 = m(x - x_1) \rightarrow y - (-4) = \frac{5}{3}(x - 2)$

$y + 4 = \frac{5}{3}(x - 2) \rightarrow 3(y + 4) = 5(x - 2) \rightarrow 3y + 12 = 5x - 10$

$3y - 5x = -10 - 12 \rightarrow 3y - 5x = -22$

26) Answer: C

$$\frac{x^2+7}{y-3} = \frac{(-5)^2+7}{7-3} = \frac{32}{4} = 8$$

27) Answer: C

Ethan paid \$3.2 for two hours and \$1.5 for each of three half-hour period after that.

$3 \times 1.5 = 4.5$

$3.2 + 4.5 = 7.7$

28) Answer: A

Cross multiply and isolate x: $\frac{c-d}{dx} = \frac{2}{7} \rightarrow 7(c-d) = 2dx \rightarrow x = \frac{7(c-d)}{2d}$

$x = \frac{7}{2}(\frac{c}{d} - \frac{d}{d}) = \frac{7}{2}(\frac{c}{d} - 1)$

29) Answer: D

$9x^4 - 4x^2 = x^2(9x^2 - 4) = x^2(3x - 2)(3x + 2)$

30) Answer: B

Factoring: $(x - 6)(x - 8) = 0 \rightarrow \begin{cases} x - 6 = 0 \rightarrow x = 6 \\ x - 8 = 0 \rightarrow x = 8 \end{cases}$

31) Answer: A

Two points are $(0,4)$ and $(10,6)$

$m = \frac{y_2-y_1}{x_2-x_1} = \frac{6-4}{10-0} = \frac{2}{10} = \frac{1}{5}$

$y - y_1 = m(x - x_1) \rightarrow y - 4 = \frac{1}{5}(x - 0)$

$y - 4 = \frac{1}{5}x \rightarrow y = \frac{1}{5}x + 4$

32) Answer: D

$\begin{cases} 3 \times (-3x + 2y = -2) \\ 2 \times (4x - 3y = 5) \end{cases} \rightarrow \begin{cases} -9x + 6y = -6 \\ 8x - 6y = 10 \end{cases}$

→add two equations:

$-x = 4 \rightarrow x = -4$

33) Answer: A

Triangle third side rule: length of the one side of a triangle is less than the sum of the lengths of the other two sides and greater than the positive difference of the lengths of the other two sides.

the third side is less than 5+8=13 and greater than 8−5=3

34) Answer: D

Mean = (111 + 120 + 127 + 140 + 159 + 165) ÷ 6 = 822 ÷ 6 = 137

Only 148 can increase the mean.

35) Answer: C

The mode is the value which occurs with the greatest frequency. Oregon and New York are greatest and the same frequency (3 times).

36) Answer: B

convert the given distance, 8 km, into centimeters, (units on the map)

8 km = 8,000 m = 800,000 cm

divide by the ratio 1:50,000.

$\frac{800,000}{50,000} = 16cm$

37) Answer: D

Area of square is: $a^2 = (\sqrt{13})^2 = 13$

38) Answer: B

$2x^4y^4 (3x^3y^3)^4 = 2x^4y^4(81x^{12}y^{12}) = 162x^{16}y^{16}$

39) Answer: C

Change percent to decimal: $25\% = 0.25 \to 0.25 \times 220 = 55$

40) Answer: D

Using the formula for mean: Mean $= \frac{sum\ of\ the\ several\ given\ values}{number\ of\ value\ given}$

$=\frac{x+(x-3)+(x-3)}{3} = \frac{3x-6}{3} = \frac{3(x-2)}{3} = x-2$

41) Answer: C

a value that is inversely proportional to another value: $a = \dfrac{k}{2b-5}$ (where k is a

constant of proportionality)

substitute a and b: $8 = \dfrac{k}{2(9)-5} \rightarrow k = 8(13) = 104; \ a = \dfrac{104}{2b-5}$

42) Answer: B

Baseballs and basketballs are spherical. The volume of sphere: $v = \dfrac{4}{3}\pi r^3$

$36\pi = \dfrac{4}{3}\pi r^3 \rightarrow 36 = \dfrac{4}{3}r^3 \rightarrow 108 = 4r^3 \rightarrow r^3 = 27 \rightarrow r = 3$

$d = 2r \rightarrow d = 2 \times 3 = 6$

43) Answer: A

Use percent formula: $\text{Part} = \dfrac{\text{percent} \times \text{whole}}{100}$

$154 = \dfrac{\text{percent} \times 140}{100} \Rightarrow \dfrac{154}{1} = \dfrac{\text{percent} \times 140}{100}$, cross multiply.

$15{,}400 = \text{percent} \times 140$, divide both sides by 140. $\rightarrow$ percent$= 110$

44) Answer: D

The sample shows that 5 out of 600 phones will be faulty. Consequently, a

proportion can be set up.

$\dfrac{5}{600} = \dfrac{P}{18{,}000}$ (P: Faulty Phone) $\rightarrow$ P $= \dfrac{5 \times 18{,}000}{600} = 150$

45) Answer: B

We can Write an equation to solve the problem.

Emma Books =Mia books +4 →Mia book = Emma – 4 = b – 4

Emma + Mia=28

b + b − 4 = 25 → 2b − 4 = 28 → 2b = 28 + 4 → b = 16

46) Answer: D

$\text{Probability} = \dfrac{number\ of\ desired\ outcomes}{number\ of\ total\ outcomes} = \dfrac{6}{11+6+7} = \dfrac{6}{24} = \dfrac{1}{4} = 0.25$

47) Answer: A

Surface Area of a cylinder = $2\pi r \, (r + h)$,

The radius of the cylinder is 4 inches, and its height are 9 inches. π is 3.14. Then:

Surface Area of a cylinder = $2 \, (3.14) \, (4) \, (4 + 9) = 326.56$ inches

48) Answer: B

use the Pythagorean theorem to find the value of unknown side.

$a^2 + b^2 = c^2 \rightarrow c^2 = 10^2 + 24^2 \rightarrow c^2 = 100 + 576 = 676 \rightarrow c = 26$

49) Answer: D

A line perpendicular to a line with slope m has a slope of $-\dfrac{1}{m}$.

So, the slope of the line perpendicular to the given line is $-\dfrac{1}{\frac{a}{b}} = -\dfrac{b}{a}$.

50) Answer: B.

For a value of x to satisfy the provided equation, it must be a solution. The equation provided should be recognized as a quadratic equation, which can be factored using many methods.

2 can be divided out of both sides: $3x^2 - 18x + 27 = 0$,

$$x^2 - 6x + 9 = 0$$

In order to further simplify this expression and solve for x, we must factor. We are looking for 2 numbers that, when multiplied together, yield +9, and when added together yield −6.

+9 factors: $\pm(1 \times 9), \pm(3 \times 3)$

$$(x - 3)(x - 3) = 0$$

$$x - 3 = 0 \rightarrow x = 3$$

So, x must equal +3. This answer can be confirmed by substituting +3 into the original equation:

$$3^2 - 6(3) + 9 = 9 - 18 + 9 = 0$$

51) Answer: A

subtracting 5 from both sides: $-\frac{(7x-3)}{3} \geq 8$

Multiply both sides by -3: $(7x - 3) \leq -24$

This operation clears the negative sign and the denominator of 3 from the left side. Add 3 to both sides and divide by 7 to isolate x:

$$7x \leq -21 \rightarrow x \leq -3$$

52) Answer: C.

Recall that dividing fractions is the same as multiplying the first fraction by its reciprocal (numerator and denominator are switched).

First rewrite the expression as a multiplication problem, switching numerator with denominator in the second fraction. Then, factor and simplify, where possible:

$$\frac{(x^2+4x+3)}{(3x^2-12x+12)} \times \frac{(x^2-5x+6)}{(x^2-2x-3)} = \frac{(x+3)(x+1)}{3(x-2)^2} \times \frac{(x-2)(x-3)}{(x-3)(x+1)} = \frac{x+3}{3(x-2)} = \frac{x+3}{3x-6}$$

53) Answer: C

If 38% of the total number of customers is female, then $100\% - 38\% = 62\%$ of the customers are male. Calculate 62% of the total. $0.62 \times 750 = 465$.

54) Answer: B

First, add the numbers given in the proportion to get a denominator: $8 + 3 = 11$.

Then, the two parts can be represented as $\frac{8}{11}$ and $\frac{3}{11}$.

The smaller share is $\frac{3}{11}$ of 66.33 kg: $\frac{3}{11} \times 66.33 \, kg = 18.09$

55) Answer: A

Since this is subtraction of 2 fractions with different denominators, their least common denominator is: $(x + 2)(4x - 1)$

$$\frac{5}{(x+2)} - \frac{2}{(4x-1)} = \frac{5(4x-1)-2(x+2)}{(x+2)(4x-1)} = \frac{20x-5-2x-4}{(x+2)(4x-1)} = \frac{18x-9}{(x+2)(4x-1)}$$

56) Answer: C

State the problem in a mathematical equation:

$$2x = 6x - 20 \rightarrow 2x - 6x = -20 \rightarrow -4x = -20 \rightarrow x = \frac{-20}{-4} = 5$$

$$6x - 20 = 6(5) - 20 = 10$$

57) Answer: C

$2h = 5p + 1$:

$$p = 3 \rightarrow 2h = 5(3) + 1 = 16 \rightarrow 2h = 16 \rightarrow h = 8$$

$$p = 5 \rightarrow 2h = 5(5) + 1 = 26 \rightarrow 2h = 26 \rightarrow h = 13$$

$$p = 11 \rightarrow 2h = 5(11) + 1 = 56 \rightarrow 2h = 56 \rightarrow h = 28$$

possible values of h: $\{8, 13, 28\}$

58) Answer: A

There are 6 digits in the repeating decimal (047619), so 4 would be the second, eighth, fourteenth digit and so on. To find the 764th digit, divide 764 by 6.

$764 \div 6 = 127$ R2

Since the remainder is 2, that means the 764th digit is the same as the 2nd digit, which is 4.

59) Answer: D

Percentage of a fraction and another fraction.

$$\frac{1}{7} = \left(\frac{x}{100}\right)\frac{5}{14} \Rightarrow \frac{1}{7} = \frac{5x}{1,400} \Rightarrow 1,400 = 35x \Rightarrow x = 40$$

60) Answer: C

Each number is the sum of the previous and the number two places to the left. Which is mean: $14 + 6 = 20$

61) Answer: C

Use the distributive property to open the parentheses and combine like terms where possible.

use FOIL method: First terms, Outside terms, Inside terms, and Last terms.

$(3y - 5x)(x + 2y) = ((3y)(x)) + ((3y)(2y)) + ((-5x)(x)) +$
$((-5x)(2y)) = 3xy + 6y^2 - 5x^2 - 10xy = -5x^2 - 7xy + 6y^2$

62) Answer: C

To solve for y, subtracting 4.23 from both sides of the equation:

$-0.5y = -0.43 - 4.23 \rightarrow -0.5y = -4.66$

Divide both sides by -0.5: $y = 9.32$

63) Answer: B

To find the area Joey needs to cover, $5 \times 14 = 70$ square feet.

Convert inches to feet: 24 inches = 2 feet.

Each board measures 2×5 feet, which equals coverage of 10 square foot.

He will need 7 of these to cover 70 square feet ($70 \div 10 = 7$).

64) Answer: D

volume of the cube: $V = S^3$

S is Side length: $90\ cm = \dfrac{90}{100} = 0.9\ m$

$V = (0.9)^3 = 0.729\ m^3$

HSPT Practice Test 4

Answers and Explanations

1) Answer: C

The smallest prime number is 2, and the largest even negative integer is −2.

2+5 (−2) = 2−10 = −8.

2) Answer: B

The difference between his income and his cost is monthly saving.

January: $3,740− $2,202= $1,538

February: $3,855 − $1,985= $1,870

March: $3,970 − $2,005 = $1,965

3) Answer: D

State the problem in a mathematical sentence:

$a + 29 = 244 − 4a$

$a + 4a = 244 − 29$

$5a = 215 \rightarrow a = 43$

4) Answer: A

$$8\frac{7}{24} − 6\frac{2}{3} + 2\frac{5}{6} = (8 − 6 + 2)\frac{7}{24} − \frac{16}{24} + \frac{20}{24} = 4(\frac{-9}{24} + \frac{20}{24}) = 4(\frac{20-9}{24}) = 4\frac{11}{24}$$

5) Answer: C

$$3^3 + 3 + 3^0 = 27 + 3 + 1 = 31$$

6) Answer: D

$$\frac{153}{170} = \frac{153}{17} \times \frac{1}{10} = 9 \times \frac{1}{10} = 0.9$$

7) Answer: A

Use the formula for Percent of Change:

$$\frac{New\ Value−Old\ Value}{Old\ Value} \times 100\ \% = \frac{32.10−30}{30} \times 100\% = \frac{2.10}{30} \times 100\% = 7\%$$

8) Answer: A

$$|2x - 3| = 7 \rightarrow \begin{cases} 2x - 3 = 7 \rightarrow 2x = 10 \rightarrow x = 5 \\ 2x - 3 = -7 \rightarrow 2x = -4 \rightarrow x = -2 \end{cases}$$

9) Answer: C

Multiply equation (2) by 5. Add two equations [(1) +5(2)]:

$$\begin{cases} 2x - 5y = 16 \\ 10x + 5y = 20 \end{cases} \rightarrow 12x = 36 \rightarrow x = 3$$

Substitute $x = 3$ into equation (1): $2(3) - 5y = 16 \rightarrow -5y = 10 \rightarrow y = -2$

10) Answer: B

3 hours equals 180 minutes.

The train passes 5 stations every 30 minutes: $\dfrac{5}{30}$

$$\dfrac{5}{30} = \dfrac{x}{180} \rightarrow x = \dfrac{180 \times 5}{30} = 30 \text{ stations}$$

11) Answer: D

Difference in percent: $16\% - 11\% = 5\% \rightarrow 5\% \times 160 = 0.05 \times 160 = 8$

12) Answer: C.

$C = \pi d = 2\pi r = 2\pi \times 18 = 36\pi$

13) Answer: C

$V = l \times w \times h = 19 \times 15 \times 8 = 2,280 \ in^3$

14) Answer: D

$$\sqrt[4]{5^{-8}} = \sqrt[4]{\dfrac{1}{5^8}} = \dfrac{\sqrt[4]{1}}{\sqrt[4]{5^8}} = \dfrac{1}{5^{\left(\frac{8}{4}\right)}} = \dfrac{1}{5^2} = 5^{-2} = \dfrac{1}{25}$$

15) Answer: A

There are no values of the variable that make the equation true.

16) Answer: C

Volume of cylinder: $V = \pi r^2 h = \pi \times 9^2 \times 8 = 648\pi$

Volume of cone: $V = \dfrac{1}{3}\pi r^2 h = \dfrac{1}{3}\pi \times 9^2 \times 6 = 162\pi$

$648\pi + 162\pi = 810\pi.$

17) Answer: D

$7.25 \times 10^{-5} = 0.0000725$

18) Answer: C

$x + 52 + 42 + 36 = 180 \rightarrow x + 130 = 180 \rightarrow x = 50$

19) Answer: B

use the Pythagorean theorem to find the value of unknown side.

$a^2 + b^2 = c^2 \rightarrow 25^2 = a^2 + 15^2 \rightarrow a^2 = 625 - 225 = 400 \rightarrow a = 20$

20) Answer: C

Use percent formula: Part $= \dfrac{\text{percent} \times \text{whole}}{100}$

Part $= \dfrac{12 \times 150}{100} = 18$

Last price: $150 + 18 = \$168$

21) Answer: A

Area of trapezoid: $\dfrac{(a+b)}{2} \times h \rightarrow A = \dfrac{(12+14)}{2} \times 10 = 130$

Area of triangle: $\dfrac{b \times h}{2} \rightarrow A = \dfrac{7 \times 10}{2} = 35$

Area of shaded region: $130 - 35 = 95$

22) Answer: D

$xy - 8x = 54 \rightarrow x(y - 8) = 54 \rightarrow 6x = 54 \rightarrow x = 9$

23) Answer: C

Multiply both sides by 4: $4 \times \left(\dfrac{x}{4}\right) = 4 \times (x - 6) \rightarrow x = 4x - 24$

Subtract both side by x and add 24 to both sides: $24 + x - x = 4x - x - 24 +$

$24 \rightarrow 3x = 24 \rightarrow x = 8$

24) Answer: D

$\begin{cases} 3 \times (-5x + 4y = 7) \\ -4 \times (-4x + 3y = 5) \end{cases} \rightarrow \begin{cases} -15x + 12y = 21 \\ 16x - 12y = -20 \end{cases}$ →add two equations:

$x = 21 - 20 \rightarrow x = 1$

25) Answer: A

There are 3 parts labeled "F" out of a total of 8 equal parts.

The probability of not spinning at "F" is 5 out of 8.

26) Answer: C

The best estimate of the product of 32 and 5.04 to the nearest whole number.

Since 32 is already a whole number and 5.04 is closer to 5 than 6. Option C is the

correct answer.

27) Answer: D

Fuel consumption rate $=\dfrac{7}{50} = 0.14$ liter per mile

Cost: $1,500 \times 0.14 \times 1.40 = 294$

28) Answer: B

Point $1(x_A, y_A) = (-6, -9)$; Point $2(x_B, y_B) = (2, -3)$

Distance between two points $= \sqrt{(x_B - x_A)^2 + (y_B - y_A)^2}$

$$\rightarrow d = \sqrt{\left(2 - (-6)\right)^2 + \left(-3 - (-9)\right)^2} = \sqrt{8^2 + 6^2} = \sqrt{64 + 36}$$

$$\rightarrow d = \sqrt{100} = 10$$

29) Answer: A

Ordered values: 75, 89, 124, 198, 225, 280, 512.

The 4th number is median.

30) Answer: D

$\sqrt{4x - 7} = 9 \rightarrow 4x - 7 = 81 \rightarrow 4x = 88 \rightarrow x = 22$

31) Answer: A

Get the equation into slop intercept form:

$y = mx + b$ where m is slope and b is y-intercept.

$x = 4y - 8$; Add 8 to both sides $\rightarrow x + 8 = 4y$; Dividing by 4: $\rightarrow y = \dfrac{1}{4}x + 2$

Thus, the y-intercept is 2.

32) Answer: C

$3^{2x} = 729 \rightarrow (3^2)^x = 729 \rightarrow 9^x = 9^3 \rightarrow x = 3$

33) Answer: C

$18: 2 \times 3 \times 3$

$64: 2 \times 2 \times 2 \times 2 \times 2 \times 2$

LCM $(18, 64) = 2 \times 2 \times 2 \times 2 \times 2 \times 2 \times 3 \times 3 = 576$

34) Answer: B

Surface area $(SA): 6a^2 \rightarrow 96 = 6a^2 \rightarrow a^2 = 16 \rightarrow a = 4cm$

Volume $(v): a^3 \rightarrow v = 4^3 = 64 \text{ cm}^3$

35) Answer: D

Write the equation into standard form: $x^2 + 2x = 35 \rightarrow x^2 + 2x - 35 = 0$

Factor this expression: $(x - 5)(x + 7) = 0 \rightarrow x = 5 \ or, x = -7 \rightarrow x^2 = \begin{cases} 25 \\ 49 \end{cases}$

36) Answer: D

The minimum amount of water: $5 \times \frac{3}{5} = 3; 3 \div 2 = 1.5$

The maximum amount of water: $5 \times \frac{3}{5} = 3$

Amount of water in all pitchers: $1.5 < w < 3$

37) Answer: C

The range is: highest value – lowest value.

R $= 65 - 17 = 48$

38) Answer: A

d $= 2r \rightarrow r = \frac{d}{2} = \frac{16}{2} = 8$

Area of circle (A): $\pi r^2 = \pi \times 8^2 = 200.96 \cong 201$

39) Answer: B

Factor the expression: $\frac{2x^2 - 15x + 7}{4(x^2 - \frac{1}{4})} = \frac{(x-7)(2x-1)}{4x^2 - 1} = \frac{(x-7)(2x-1)}{(2x-1)(2x+1)} = \frac{x-7}{2x+1}$

40) Answer: D

$$\left(\frac{1}{3}\right)^{-4} = \frac{1}{3^{-4}} = 3^4 = 81$$

41) Answer: B

$$\frac{(5x^{-3}y^4)^3}{100y^{-2}z^2} = \frac{125x^{-9}y^{12}}{100y^{-2}z^2} = \frac{5y^{14}}{4x^9z^2}$$

42) Answer: D

Rate: $\frac{\$1}{1\text{Kg}} = \frac{100\cent}{1,000g} \rightarrow 1\,^\$/_{kg} = 0.1\,^\cent/_g$

The price is: $30 \times 0.1 = 3$cent per kilogram.

43) Answer: C

$3P = 6 \rightarrow P = 2$ The price of 2007 is one-third of 2012 $(6 \div 3 = 2)$

44) Answer: D

First equation: $4y + 5 = 20x + 9 \rightarrow 4y = 20x + 4 \rightarrow y = 5x + 1 \rightarrow m_1 = 5$

Second question: $5y + 4 = x + 7 \rightarrow 5y = x + 3 \rightarrow y = \frac{1}{5}x + \frac{3}{5} \rightarrow m_2 = \frac{1}{5}$

$m_1 = 5$ and $m_2 = \frac{1}{5}$, they aren't equal slopes or negative reciprocals.

45) Answer: C

Area $= 5\frac{1}{3} \times 8\frac{2}{5} = \frac{16}{3} \times \frac{42}{5} = \frac{672}{15} = \frac{672}{15}$ square feet.

One-fourth $= \frac{672}{15} \div 4 = \frac{224}{5} \times \frac{1}{4} = \frac{224}{20} = \frac{112}{10} = 11.2$

46) Answer: A

Two points are $(2, 2)$ and $(-4, -1)$

$\rightarrow m = \frac{y_2 - y_1}{x_2 - x_1} = \frac{-1-2}{-4-2} = \frac{-3}{-6} = \frac{1}{2}$

47) Answer: B

$V = \left(\frac{base \times height}{2}\right) \times \text{height of prism} \rightarrow V = \left(\frac{10 \times 15}{2}\right) \times 5 = 375$

48) Answer: C

$f(a) = 4a - 7$ and $f(a) = -19$: $4a - 7 = -19$ so that $4a = -12$ and $a = -3$.

$f(b) = 4b - 7$ and $f(b) = 9$: $4b - 7 = 9$ so that $4b = 16$ and $b = 4$

Finally, f(a + b) = f(−3 + 4) = f(1)

f(1) = 4(1) − 7 = −3.

49) Answer: D

The ratio of $x : y$ is equivalent to x divided by y, or $\frac{x}{y}$.

Equation: $28x = 12y$

Dividing both sides by 28: $x = \frac{12y}{28}$

Dividing both sides by y: $\frac{x}{y} = \frac{12}{28} = \frac{3}{7}$

Then, $x : y$ is $3 : 7$

50) Answer: B

Method 1:

The formula for measurement of each angle of a regular polygon:

$x = \frac{180(n-2)}{n}$, (x is the measurement of the interior angle; n is the number of sides)

Substituting the given information:

$\frac{180(n-2)}{n} = 168 \rightarrow 180n - 360 = 168n \rightarrow 180n - 168n = 360$

$\rightarrow 12n = 360 \rightarrow n = 30$; The polygon has 30 angles and 30 sides.

Method 2:

The sum of exterior angles of any polygon is always equal to 360 degrees.

Exterior angle(degrees) × n = 360; (n, is the number of angles (sides)).

Exterior angle = 180 – interior angle

The exterior angle = 180 – 168 = 12 degrees.

Then, $12n = 360 \rightarrow n = 360 \div 12 = 30$

The polygon has 30 angles and 30 sides.

51) Answer: C

Age of Jim: x and the age of Jim 4 years ago: $x - 4$

The age of Frank: $5x$ and the age of Frank 4 years ago: $5x - 4$

$(x-4)(5x-4) = 21$

$5x^2 - 4x - 20x + 16 = 21 \rightarrow 5x^2 - 24x - 5 = 0$

$(5x+1)(x-5) = 0$

$5x + 1 = 0$ will yield a negative value for x, so this is not possible solution.

$x - 5 = 0 \rightarrow x = 5 \rightarrow$The age of Frank: $5x = 5(5) = 25$.

52) Answer: B

$\frac{d}{4} = \frac{16}{d}$ Cross-multiply: $d \times d = 4 \times 16 \rightarrow d^2 = 64$

Then, find the square root of both sides:

The actual square root of d^2 is $\pm d$ and the actual square root of 64 is ± 8, so:

$d = \pm 8$

Of the answer choices for this question, -8 is the best choice since it is the only one that is true about the equation.

53) Answer: A

Let f be the points earned by FT, r be the points scored by RT, and g be the points scored by GT.

f $= 25\% \; of \; 220 = 0.25 \times 220 = 55$ points

$220 = f + r + g \rightarrow 220 = 55 + 4g + g \rightarrow 220 - 55 = 5g$

$\rightarrow 5g = 165 \rightarrow g = 33; r = 4g \rightarrow r = 4(33) = 132$ points

54) Answer: A

If x is the smaller consecutive integer, then $x + 1$ is the larger consecutive integer. Use their sum (-23) to find x:

$$x + (x + 1) = -23 \rightarrow 2x + 1 = -23 \rightarrow 2x = -24 \rightarrow x = -12$$

The two consecutive integers are -12 and -11.

three is added to the smaller integer: $-12 + 5 = -7$

and 1 is subtracted from the larger integer: $-11 - 3 = -14$

Find the product: $(-7)(-14) = 98$

55) Answer: B

The total number of handballs in the container is: $25 + 18 + 7 + 8 + 19 = 77$

Since there are 7 green handballs, the probability of selecting a green handball is

$\frac{7}{77} = \frac{1}{11}$

56) Answer: A

$8 + (3n + 11) - (10n + 5) = 8 + 3n + 11 - 10n - 5 = 14 - 7n$

57) Answer: C

Jimmy has 98 pages left to read ($106 - 8$). $\frac{8}{15} = \frac{32}{60}$

He read at a rate of 32 pages per 1 hour. Then, divide the total number of pages remaining (98) by the number of pages he can read per hour (32):

$\frac{98}{32} = 3\frac{1}{16}$

58) Answer: B

Two parallel lines (m & side BC) intersected by side AB.

$n = 65°$ (Interior angles)

59) Answer: D

Let x represent the number of pounds that can be bought for $18.00.

$\frac{1}{3.60} = \frac{x}{18}$

Cross multiply and solve the equation: $3.60x = 18 \rightarrow x = \frac{18}{3.60} = 5$

60) Answer: B

Let x represent the distance you are trying to find (in km).

The quickest way to solve for x is to create a proportion with the quantities you do know. $\frac{km\ on\ ground}{cm\ on\ map}$; Substitute the numbers you know: $\frac{4}{20} = \frac{x}{32}$

Cross-multiply to get this equation and solve:

$4 \times 32 = 20x \rightarrow x = \frac{128}{20} = 6.4$

61) Answer: C

To write a percent, move the decimal point two places to the right and follow the resulting number with the % sign. Or adding the % sign after multiplying the decimal number and 100: $0.056 \times 100 = 5.6\% = 5.60\%$

62) Answer: A

$\frac{(90-x)}{7} = 2x \rightarrow 90 - x = 7(2x) \rightarrow 90 = 14x + x \rightarrow x = \frac{90}{15} = 6$

63) Answer: C

Base salary: $52,000.

Health benefits: $52,000 \times 15\% = \$52,000 \times 0.15 = \$7,800$.

Her base salary, plus benefits: $52,000 + \$7,800 = \$59,800$.

Since her total compensation: $64,000; Bonus: $64,000 – \$59,800 = \$4,200$.

Calculate the percent of her bonus: $\frac{4,200}{59,800} = \frac{x}{100} \rightarrow x = \frac{420,000}{59,800} = 7.0$

64) Answer: B

Note: "@" and "#" are two "operations", and they are defined in the first two lines of the question.

Begin by evaluating $f(-3)$ and $f(2)$, Then, substitute $f(-3)$ and $f(2)$ into the first operation and substitute the appropriate values into the second operation.

$f(-3) = 2(-3)^2 - 14 = 18 - 14 = 4$

$f(2) = 2(2)^2 - 14 = 8 - 14 = -6$

$a @ b = a - 2ab:$

$(f(-3)@ f(2)) = (4)@(-6) = (4) - 2(4)(-6) = 4 + 48 = 52$

$a\#b = a - 4b^2: f(-3) = 2(-3)^2 - 14 = 4$

$(f(-3)@ f(2))\#f(-3) = (52)\#f(-3) = (52)\#(4) = 52 - 4(4)^2 = 52 - 4(16) = 52 - 64 = -12$

HSPT Practice Test 5

Answers and Explanations

1) Answer: C

$\frac{-26}{3} = -8.7$ and $\frac{75}{8} = 9.4$, then the even numbers are:

$(-8, -6, -4, -2, 0, 2, 4, 6, 8)$

2) Answer: D

The distance between two points always is positive. Use formula:

AB = |b − a| or |a − b| → | − 8 − 7| or |7 − (−8)| = |7 + 8|

3) Answer: B

Sum of the measures of the angles of a triangle is 180, if two angles are 60 then the third one is 60, then the triangle is equilateral triangle, and all side are equal.

4) Answer: A

All factors of 24 are: 1, 2, 3, 4, 6, 8, 12, 24, then sum of them is 60.

5) Answer: B

$$\frac{1}{6} + \frac{3}{8} = \frac{4}{24} + \frac{9}{24} = \frac{13}{24}$$

$$1 - \frac{13}{24} = \frac{24}{24} - \frac{13}{24} = \frac{11}{24}$$

6) Answer: B

Each next term after first term is found by multiplying the previous term by $\frac{1}{20}$,

then the choice B is correct.

7) Answer: A

Start to list factors of each number:

Factors of 16: 1, 2, 4, 8, 16

Factors of 20: 1, 2, 4, 5, 10, 20

Factors of 27: 1, 3, 9, 27

The greatest common factor is 1.

8) Answer: B

4 more: $+4$

Ratio: $\div$; Ratio of a number to 5: $\frac{x}{5}$

7 less: -7 ; 7 less than the number: $x - 7$

$4 + \frac{x}{5} = x - 7$

9) Answer: A

Rewriting each fraction with common denominator or converting each fraction to decimal and order the decimal from least to greatest.

$\frac{3}{7} = 0.43$ $\qquad$ $\frac{5}{9} = 0.56$ $\quad$ $\frac{1}{3} = 0.33$ $\qquad$ $\frac{19}{21} = 0.9$ $\qquad$ $\frac{11}{18} = 0.61$

10) Answer: B

calculating Elena's total earnings:

35 hours $\times$ \$9.20 an hour = \$322

Next, divide this total by her brother's hourly rate:

\$322 $\div$ \$11.50 = 28 hours

11) Answer: C

number of fiction books: x

number of nonfiction books: $x + 1{,}200$

Total number of books: $x + (x + 12{,}000)$

40% of the total number of books are fiction, therefore:

$40\%[x + (x + 1{,}200)] = x \rightarrow 0.4(2x + 1{,}200) = x$

$0.8x + 480 = x \ \rightarrow 480 = x - 0.8x \rightarrow 0.2x = 480$

$\rightarrow x = 2{,}400$ number of fictions

$x + 1{,}200 = 2{,}400 + 1{,}200 = 3{,}600$, the number of nonfiction books

$2{,}400 + 3{,}600 = 6{,}000$, the total number of books in the library

12) Answer: B

The scale is: 5 cm:1km, (5 cm on the map represents an actual distance of 1 km).

first necessary to rewrite the scale ratio in terms of units squared:

5^2cm square:1^2km square, which gives $25\ cm^2 : 1\ km^2$

Then, $\dfrac{25\ cm^2}{1km^2} = \dfrac{80\ cm^2}{x\ km^2}$, (where x is the unknown actual area).

Every proportion you write should maintain consistency in the ratios described (km^2 both occupy the denominator).

Cross-multiply and isolate to solve for the unknown area x:

$x.\dfrac{25\ cm^2}{1km^2} = 80\ cm^2 \rightarrow x = 80\ cm^2.\dfrac{1\ km^2}{25\ cm^2} \rightarrow x = 3.2\ km^2$

13) Answer: B

move decimal point in divisor so last digit is in the unit place (0.4 to 4)

move decimal point in dividend same number of places to the right,

(12.24 to 122.4)

divide (1224 ÷ 04)=306

insert a decimal point into the answer above the decimal point in the dividend

(30.6)

14) Answer: B

Circumference= $2\pi r = 2 \times \pi \times 8 = 16\pi$

15) Answer: C

Be careful with the conversion factor (per hundred gallons; NOT per gallon).

$23,700 \times \dfrac{0.95}{100} = 225.15$

$225.15 + 4.20 = 229.35$

16) Answer: A

$\dfrac{(x^3 - x^2)}{(x^2 - x)} = \dfrac{x^2(x - 1)}{x(x - 1)} = x$

17) Answer: C

For odd index we can have negative radicand.

In the even index, negative radicand is undefined.

$\sqrt{-81}$ has a negative number under the even index, so it is non-real.

Negative numbers don't have real square roots, because negative and positive integer squared is either positive or 0.

18) Answer: D

$3f(2a) = 540 \rightarrow$ (divide by 3): $f(2a) = 180$

(subtitute 2a) $5(2a)^2 = 180 \rightarrow$ (divide by 5): $(2a)^2 = 36 \rightarrow 4a^2 = 36 \rightarrow$

$a^2 = 9 \rightarrow a = 3$

19) Answer: A

2 hours and 30 minutes is 2.5 hour.

$R \times T = D \rightarrow 110 \times 2.5 = D \rightarrow D = 275$ miles

20) Answer: B

$10x - 7 \le 6x + 5 \rightarrow Add\ 7: 10x - 7 + 7 \le 6x + 5 + 7 \rightarrow$

$subtract\ 6x: 10x - 6x \le 12 \rightarrow -4x \le 12 \rightarrow x \ge -3$

21) Answer: B

Use formula to raise a number: $(x^a)^b = x^{ab}$

$3^4 = (3^2)^2 = 9^2$

22) Answer: C

Simple interest rate: I = prt (I = interest, p = principal, r = rate, t = time)

$I = 3,800 \times 0.045 \times 3 = 513$

23) Answer: D

A straight angle is an angle measured exactly $180°$

$$55° + 30° = 85°$$

$$180° - 85° = 95°$$

24) Answer: C

$$\frac{32x^5y^7z^{-2}}{12\ x^2y^9z^0} = \frac{32}{12} \times \frac{x^5}{x^2} \times \frac{y^7}{y^9} \times \frac{z^{-2}}{z^0} = \frac{8}{3} \times x^3 \times \frac{1}{y^2} \times \frac{1}{z^2} = \frac{8x^3}{3\ y^2z^2}$$

25) Answer: B

$m = \frac{y_2 - y_1}{x_2 - x_1} = \frac{2 - (-1)}{4 - 2} = \frac{3}{2}$

$y - y_1 = m(x - x_1) \rightarrow y - (-1) = \frac{3}{2}(x - 2)$

$y + 1 = \frac{3}{2}(x - 2) \rightarrow 2(y + 1) = 3(x - 2) \rightarrow 2y + 2 = 3x - 6$

$2y - 3x = -6 - 2 \rightarrow 2y - 3x = -8$

26) Answer: C

$\frac{x^2 + 5}{y + 1} = \frac{(-2)^2 + 5}{2 + 1} = \frac{9}{3} = 3$

27) Answer: C

Ethan paid $3.5 for two hours and $0.75 for each of three half-hour period after

that.

$3 \times 0.75 = 2.25$

$3.5 + 2.25 = 5.75$

28) Answer: A

Cross multiply and isolate x: $\frac{c-d}{dx} = \frac{2}{3} \rightarrow 3(c - d) = 2dx \rightarrow x = \frac{3(c-d)}{2d}$

$x = \frac{3}{2}(\frac{c}{d} - \frac{d}{d}) = \frac{3}{2}(\frac{c}{d} - 1)$

29) Answer: D

$x^3 - x = x(x^2 - 1) = x(x - 1)(x + 1)$

30) Answer: B

Factoring: $(x - 4)(x - 6) = 0 \rightarrow \begin{cases} x - 4 = 0 \rightarrow x = 4 \\ x - 6 = 0 \rightarrow x = 6 \end{cases}$

31) Answer: A

Two points are $(0,2)$ and $(6,5)$; $m = \frac{y_2 - y_1}{x_2 - x_1} = \frac{5 - 2}{6 - 0} = \frac{3}{6} = \frac{1}{2}$

$y - y_1 = m(x - x_1) \rightarrow y - 2 = \frac{1}{2}(x - 0)$

$y - 2 = \frac{1}{2}x \rightarrow y = \frac{1}{2}x + 2$

32) Answer: D

$$\begin{cases} 5 \times (-3x + 4y = -5) \\ 4 \times (2x - 5y = 8) \end{cases} \rightarrow \begin{cases} -15x + 20y = -25 \\ 8x - 20y = 32 \end{cases} \rightarrow \text{add two equations:}$$

$-7x = 7 \rightarrow x = -1$

33) Answer: A

Triangle third side rule: length of the one side of a triangle is less than the sum of the lengths of the other two sides and greater than the positive difference of the lengths of the other two sides.

the third side is less than 5+8=13 and greater than 8-5=3

34) Answer: D

Mean = $(118 + 134 + 148 + 151 + 159 + 184) \div 6 = 894 \div 6 = 149$

Only 159 can increase the mean.

35) Answer: C

The mode is the value which occurs with the greatest frequency. New York and Ohio are greatest and the same frequency (3 times).

36) Answer: B

convert the given distance, 6 km, into centimeters, (units on the map)

6 km = 6,000 m = 600,000 cm; divide by the ratio 1:50,000.

$\frac{600,000}{50,000} = 12$ cm

37) Answer: D

Area of square is: $a^2 = (\sqrt{5})^2 = 5$

38) Answer: B

$2x^4y^3 (4x^3y^0)^3 = 2x^4y^3(64x^9) = 128x^{13}y^3$

39) Answer: C

Change percent to decimal: $18\% = 0.18$

$0.18 \times 250 = 45$

40) Answer: D

Using the formula for mean: Mean $= \dfrac{\text{sum of the several given values}}{\text{number of value given}}$

$= \dfrac{x+(x-3)+(x-3)}{3} = \dfrac{3x-6}{3} = \dfrac{3(x-2)}{3} = x-2$

41) Answer: C

a value that is inversely proportional to another value: $a = \dfrac{k}{2b-5}$ (where k is a

constant of proportionality)

substitute a and b: $15 = \dfrac{k}{2(7)-5} \rightarrow k = 15(9) = 135 \rightarrow a = \dfrac{135}{2b-5}$

42) Answer: B

Baseballs and basketballs are spherical. The volume of sphere: $v = \dfrac{4}{3}\pi r^3$

$36\pi = \dfrac{4}{3}\pi r^3 \rightarrow 36 = \dfrac{4}{3}r^3 \rightarrow 108 = 4r^3 \rightarrow r^3 = 27 \rightarrow r = 3$

$d = 2r \rightarrow d = 2 \times 3 = 6$

43) Answer: A

Use percent formula: Part $= \dfrac{\text{percent} \times \text{whole}}{100}$

$221 = \dfrac{\text{percent} \times 170}{100} \Rightarrow \dfrac{221}{1} = \dfrac{\text{percent} \times 170}{100}$, cross multiply.

$22{,}100 = \text{percent} \times 170$, divide both sides by 170. $\rightarrow$ percent$= 130$

44) Answer: D

The sample shows that 3 out of 200 phones will be faulty. Consequently, a

proportion can be set up.

$\dfrac{3}{200} = \dfrac{P}{12{,}000}$ (P: Faulty Phone) $\rightarrow$ P $= \dfrac{3 \times 12{,}000}{200} = 180$

45) Answer: B

We can Write an equation to solve the problem.

Emma Books =Mia books +5 →Mia book = Emma – 5=b-5

Emma + Mia=17

$$b + b - 5 = 17 \rightarrow 2b - 5 = 17 \rightarrow 2b = 17 + 5 \rightarrow b = 11$$

46) Answer: D

$$\text{Probability} = \frac{number\ of\ desired\ outcomes}{number\ of\ total\ outcomes} = \frac{4}{5+4+7} = \frac{4}{16} = \frac{1}{4} = 0.25$$

47) Answer: A

Surface Area of a cylinder = 2πr (r + h),

The radius of the cylinder is 6 inches, and its height are 9 inches. π is 3.14. Then:

Surface Area of a cylinder = 2 (3.14) (6) (6 + 9) = 565.2 inches

48) Answer: B

use the Pythagorean theorem to find the value of unknown side.

$$a^2 + b^2 = c^2 \rightarrow c^2 = 20^2 + 15^2 \rightarrow a^2 = 400 + 225 = 625 \rightarrow c = 25$$

49) Answer: D

A line perpendicular to a line with slope m has a slope of $-\frac{1}{m}$.

So, the slope of the line perpendicular to the given line is $-\frac{1}{\frac{c}{d}} = -\frac{d}{c}$.

50) Answer: B.

For a value of x to satisfy the provided equation, it must be a solution. The equation provided should be recognized as a quadratic equation, which can be factored using many methods.

3 can be divided out of both sides: $3x^2 - 18x + 27 = 0$,

$$x^2 - 6x + 9 = 0$$

In order to further simplify this expression and solve for x, we must factor. We are looking for 2 numbers that, when multiplied together, yield +9, and when added together yield −6.

+9 factors: $\pm(1 \times 9), \pm(3 \times 3)$

$$(x - 3)(x - 3) = 0$$

$$x - 3 = 0 \rightarrow x = 3$$

So, x must equal $+3$. This answer can be confirmed by substituting $+3$ into the original equation:

$$3^2 - 6(3) + 9 = 9 - 18 + 9 = 0$$

51) Answer: A

subtracting 6 from both sides: $-\frac{(5x-8)}{4} \geq 2$

Multiply both sides by -4: $(5x - 8) \leq -8$

This operation clears the negative sign and the denominator of 4 from the left side. Add 8 to both sides and divide by 5 to isolate x:

$$5x \leq 0 \rightarrow x \leq 0$$

52) Answer: C.

Recall that dividing fractions is the same as multiplying the first fraction by its reciprocal (numerator and denominator are switched).

First rewrite the expression as a multiplication problem, switching numerator with denominator in the second fraction. Then, factor and simplify, where possible:

$$\frac{(x^2+5x+6)}{(2x^2-8x+8)} \times \frac{(x^2-3x+2)}{(x^2+2x-3)} = \frac{(x+2)(x+3)}{2(x-2)^2} \times \frac{(x-2)(x-1)}{(x-1)(x+3)} = \frac{x+2}{2(x-2)} = \frac{x+2}{2x-4}$$

53) Answer: C

If 38% of the total number of customers is female, then $100\% - 38\% = 62\%$ of the customers are male. Calculate 62% of the total.

$0.62 \times 950 = 589$.

54) Answer: B

First, add the numbers given in the proportion to get a denominator: $8 + 3 = 11$.

Then, the two parts can be represented as $\frac{8}{11}$ and $\frac{3}{11}$.

The smaller share is $\frac{3}{11}$ of 54.5 kg: $\frac{3}{11} \times 54.5 \, kg = 14.86$

55) Answer: A

Since this is subtraction of 2 fractions with different denominators, their least common denominator is: $(x-2)(3x+1)$

$$\frac{5}{(x-2)} - \frac{6}{(3x+1)} = \frac{5(3x+1)-6(x-2)}{(x-2)(3x+1)} = \frac{15x+5-6x+12}{(x-2)(3x+1)} = \frac{9x+17}{(x-2)(3x+1)}$$

56) Answer: C

State the problem in a mathematical equation:

$$2x = 5x - 18 \rightarrow 2x - 5x = -18 \rightarrow -3x = -18 \rightarrow x = \frac{-18}{-3} = 6$$

$$5x - 18 = 5(6) - 18 = 12$$

57) Answer: C

$3h = 2p + 2$:

$p = 2 \rightarrow 3h = 2(2) + 2 = 6 \rightarrow 3h = 6 \rightarrow h = 2$

$p = 5 \rightarrow 3h = 2(5) + 2 = 12 \rightarrow 3h = 12 \rightarrow h = 4$

$p = 11 \rightarrow 3h = 2(11) + 2 = 24 \rightarrow 3h = 24 \rightarrow h = 8$

possible values of h: {2,4,8}

58) Answer: A

There are 6 digits in the repeating decimal (142857), so 1 would be the first, seventh, thirteenth digit and so on.

To find the 391st digit, divide 391 by 6.

$391 \div 6 = 65$ R1

Since the remainder is 1, that means the 391st digit is the same as the 1st digit, which is 1.

59) Answer: D

Percentage of a fraction and another fraction.

$$\frac{2}{5} = \left(\frac{x}{100}\right)\frac{5}{7} \Rightarrow \frac{2}{5} = \frac{5x}{700} \Rightarrow 1,400 = 25x \Rightarrow x = 56$$

60) Answer: C

Each number is the sum of the previous and the number 2 places to the left.

Which is mean: $16 + 9 = 25$

61) Answer: C

Use the distributive property to open the parentheses and combine like terms where possible.

use FOIL method: First terms, Outside terms, Inside terms, and Last terms.

$(3y - x)(x - 2y) = (3y.x) + (3y.-2y) + (-x.x) + (-x.-2y)$

$= 3xy - 6y^2 - x^2 + 2xy = -x^2 + 5xy - 6y^2$

62) Answer: C

To solve for y, subtracting 3.98 from both sides of the equation:

$-0.8y = -0.86 - 1.87 \rightarrow -0.6y = -2.73$

Divide both sides by -0.6: $y = 4.55$

63) Answer: B

To find the area Joey needs to cover, $8 \times 9 = 72$ square feet.

Convert inches to feet: 6 inches = 0.5 feet.

Each board measures 0.5×4 feet, which equals coverage of 2 square foot.

He will need 36 of these to cover 72 square feet ($72 \div 2 = 36$).

64) Answer: D

volume of the cube: $V = S^3$

S is Side length: $140 \, cm = \frac{140}{100} = 1.4 \, m$

$V = (1.4)^3 = 2.744 \, m^3$

HSPT Practice Test 6
Answers and Explanations

1) Answer: C

The smallest prime number is 2, and the largest even negative integer is -2.

$2+3\,(-2) = 2-6 = -4$.

2) Answer: B

The difference between his income and his cost is monthly saving.

January: $\$3,025 - \$1,870 = \$1,155$

February: $\$3,405 - \$1,916 = \$1,489$

March: $\$3,280 - \$1,962 = \$1,318$

3) Answer: D

State the problem in a mathematical sentence:

$a + 42 = 230 - 3a$

$a + 3a = 230 - 42$

$4a = 188 \rightarrow a = 47$

4) Answer: A

$$4\frac{1}{21} - 5\frac{4}{7} + 2\frac{1}{3} = (4-5+2)\frac{1}{21} - \frac{12}{21} + \frac{7}{21} = 1\frac{1}{21} - \frac{5}{21} = \frac{22}{21} - \frac{5}{21} = \frac{17}{21}$$

5) Answer: C

$3^3 + 3^2 + 3 = 27 + 9 + 3 = 39$

6) Answer: D

$$\frac{108}{270} = \frac{108}{27} \times \frac{1}{10} = 4 \times \frac{1}{10} = 0.4$$

7) Answer: A

Use the formula for Percent of Change,

$$\frac{\text{New Value} - \text{Old Value}}{\text{Old Value}} \times 100\,\% = \frac{31.50-30}{30} \times 100\% = \frac{1.50}{30} \times 100\% = 5\%$$

8) Answer: A

$$|2x - 3| = 5 \rightarrow \begin{cases} 2x - 3 = 5 \rightarrow 2x = 8 \rightarrow x = 4 \\ 2x - 3 = -5 \rightarrow 2x = -2 \rightarrow x = -1 \end{cases}$$

9) Answer: C

Multiply equation (2) by 3. Add two equations [(1) +3(2)]:

$$\begin{cases} x - 3y = 1 \\ 6x + 3y = 6 \end{cases} \rightarrow 7x = 7 \rightarrow x = 1$$

Substitute $x = 1$ into equation (1): $1 - 3y = 1 \rightarrow -3y = 0 \rightarrow y = 0$

10) Answer: B

2 hours equals 120 minutes. The train passes 4 stations every 15 minutes: $\frac{4}{15}$

$$\frac{4}{15} = \frac{x}{120} \rightarrow x = \frac{120 \times 4}{15} = 32 \text{ stations}$$

11) Answer: D

Difference in percent: $8\% - 6\% = 2\%$

$2\% \times 180 = 0.02 \times 180 = 3.60$

12) Answer: C.

$C = \pi d = 2\pi r = 2\pi \times 43 = 86\,\pi$

13) Answer: C

$V = l \times w \times h = 19 \times 12 \times 9 = 2,052 \; in^3$

14) Answer: D

$$\sqrt[4]{4^{-8}} = \sqrt[4]{\frac{1}{4^8}} = \frac{\sqrt[4]{1}}{\sqrt[4]{4^8}} = \frac{1}{4^{\left(\frac{8}{4}\right)}} = \frac{1}{4^2} = 4^{-2} = \frac{1}{16}$$

15) Answer: A

There are no values of the variable that make the equation true.

16) Answer: C

Volume of cylinder: $V = \pi r^2 h = \pi \times 8^2 \times 12 = 768\pi$

Volume of cone: $V = \frac{1}{3}\pi r^2 h = \frac{1}{3}\pi \times 8^2 \times 6 = 128\pi$

$768\pi + 128\pi = 896\pi.$

17) Answer: D

$3.21 \times 10^{-4} = 0.000321$

18) Answer: C

$x + 53 + 32 + 45 = 180 \rightarrow x + 130 = 180 \rightarrow x = 50$

19) Answer: B

use the Pythagorean theorem to find the value of unknown side.

$a^2 + b^2 = c^2 \rightarrow 20^2 = a^2 + 12^2 \rightarrow a^2 = 400 - 144 = 256 \rightarrow a = 16$

20) Answer: C

Use percent formula: Part $= \frac{\text{percent} \times \text{whole}}{100} \rightarrow$ Part $= \frac{18 \times 250}{100} = 45$

Last price: $250 + 45 = \$295$

21) Answer: A

Area of trapezoid: $\frac{(a+b)}{2} \times h \rightarrow A = \frac{(12+14)}{2} \times 9 = 117$

Area of triangle: $\frac{b \times h}{2} \rightarrow A = \frac{8 \times 9}{2} = 36$

Area of shaded region: $117 - 36 = 81$

22) Answer: D

$xy - 5x = 32 \rightarrow x(y - 5) = 32$

$8x = 32 \rightarrow x = 4$

23) Answer: C

Multiply both sides by 3: $3 \times \left(\frac{x}{3}\right) = 3 \times (x - 4) \rightarrow x = 3x - 12$

Subtract both side by x and add 12 to both sides: $12 + x - x = 3x + x - 12 +$

$12 \rightarrow 4x = 12 \rightarrow x = 3$

24) Answer: D

$\begin{cases} 3 \times (-5x + 2y = 20) \\ -2 \times (-4x + 3y = 9) \end{cases} \rightarrow \begin{cases} -15x + 6y = 60 \\ 8x - 6y = -18 \end{cases} \rightarrow$ add two equations:

$-7x = 42 \rightarrow x = -6$

25) Answer: A

There are 3 parts labeled "F" out of a total of 8 equal parts.

The probability of not spinning at "F" is 5 out of 8.

26) Answer: C

The best estimate of the product of 23 and 2.08 to the nearest whole number.

Since 23 is already a whole number and 2.08 is closer to 2 than 3. Option C is the correct answer.

27) Answer: D

Fuel consumption rate $= \frac{12}{75} = 0.16$ liter per mile

Cost: $1,700 \times 0.16 \times 1.05 = 285.60$

28) Answer: B

Point $1(x_A, y_A) = (-2, -7)$; Point $2(x_B, y_B) = (6, -1)$

Distance between two points $= \sqrt{(x_B - x_A)^2 + (y_B - y_A)^2}$

$$\rightarrow d = \sqrt{\left(6 - (-2)\right)^2 + \left(-1 - (-7)\right)^2} = \sqrt{8^2 + 6^2} = \sqrt{64 + 36}$$

$$\rightarrow d = \sqrt{100} = 10$$

29) Answer: A

Ordered values: 122, 122, 165, 186, 212, 318, 334.

The 4th number is median.

30) Answer: D

$\sqrt{3x - 1} = 4 \rightarrow 3x + 1 = 16 \rightarrow 3x = 15 \rightarrow x = 5$

31) Answer: A

Get the equation into slop intercept form:

$y = mx + b$ where m is slope and b is y-intercept.

$x = 2y - 4$; Add 4 to both sides $\rightarrow x + 4 = 2y$; Dividing by 2: $\rightarrow y = \frac{1}{2}x + 2$

Thus, the y-intercept is 2.

32) Answer: C

$3^{2x} = 81 \rightarrow (3^2)^x = 81 \rightarrow 9^x = 9^2 \rightarrow x = 2$

33) Answer: C

$24: 2 \times 2 \times 2 \times 3$

$30: 2 \times 3 \times 5$

LCM $(30, 24) = 2 \times 2 \times 2 \times 3 \times 5 = 120$

34) Answer: B

Surface area $(SA): 6a^2 \rightarrow 54 = 6a^2 \rightarrow a^2 = 9 \rightarrow a = 3$ cm

Volume $(v): a^3 \rightarrow v = 3^3 = 27$ cm^3

35) Answer: D

Write the equation into standard form: $x^2 + x = 30 \rightarrow x^2 + x - 30 = 0$

Factor this expression: $(x - 5)(x + 6) = 0 \rightarrow x = 5 \; or, x = -6 \rightarrow x^2 = \begin{cases} 25 \\ 36 \end{cases}$

36) Answer: D

The minimum amount of water: $5 \times \frac{3}{5} = 3; \; 3 \div 2 = 1.5$

The maximum amount of water: $5 \times \frac{3}{5} = 3$

Amount of water in all pitchers: $1.5 < w < 3$

37) Answer: C

The range is: highest value – lowest value.

R $= 45 - 28 = 17$

38) Answer: A

$d = 2r \rightarrow r = \frac{d}{2} = \frac{14}{2} = 7$

Area of circle (A): $\pi r^2 = \pi \times 7^2 = 153.9$

39) Answer: B

Factor the expression: $\frac{2x^2 - 7x - 4}{4(x^2 - \frac{1}{4})} = \frac{(x-4)(2x+1)}{4x^2 - 1} = \frac{(x-4)(2x+1)}{(2x-1)(2x+1)} = \frac{x-4}{2x-1}$

40) Answer: D

$$\left(\frac{1}{3}\right)^{-3} = \frac{1}{3^{-3}} = 3^3 = 27$$

41) Answer: B

$$\frac{(5x^{-2}y^3)^2}{125y^{-2}z^{-1}} = \frac{25x^{-4}y^6}{125y^{-2}z^{-1}} = \frac{y^8z}{5x^4}$$

42) Answer: D

Rate: $\frac{\$1}{1Kg} = \frac{100¢}{1,000g} \rightarrow 1\,\$/_{kg} = 0.1\,¢/_g$

The price is: $10 \times 0.1 = 1$cent per kilogram.

43) Answer: C

$2P = 2 \rightarrow P = 1$ The price of 2007 is half of 2012 $(2 \div 2 = 1)$

44) Answer: D

First equation: $2y - 1 = 4x + 5 \rightarrow 2y = 4x + 6 \rightarrow y = 2x + 3 \rightarrow m_1 = 2$

Second question: $4y - 1 = 2x + 5 \rightarrow 4y = 2x + 6 \rightarrow y = \frac{1}{2}x + \frac{3}{2} \rightarrow m_2 = \frac{1}{2}$

$m_1 = 2$ and $m_2 = \frac{1}{2}$, they aren't equal slopes or negative reciprocals.

45) Answer: C

Area$= 9\frac{1}{2} \times 7\frac{1}{5} = \frac{19}{2} \times \frac{36}{5} = \frac{684}{10} = \frac{342}{5}$ square feet.

One-fourth $= \frac{342}{5} \div 4 = \frac{342}{5} \times \frac{1}{4} = \frac{342}{20} = \frac{171}{10} = 17.10$

46) Answer: A

Two points are $(6,6)$ and $(-10,-2) \rightarrow m = \frac{y_2 - y_1}{x_2 - x_1} = \frac{-2-6}{-10-6} = \frac{-8}{-16} = \frac{1}{2}$

47) Answer: B

$V = \left(\frac{base \times height}{2}\right) \times$ height of prism $\rightarrow V = \left(\frac{9 \times 15}{2}\right) \times 4 = 270$

48) Answer: C

f(a) $= 5a - 2$ and f(a) $= -12$: $5a - 2 = -12$ so that $5a = -10$ and $a = -2$.

f(b) $= 5b - 2$ and f(b) $= 13$: $5b - 2 = 13$ so that $5b = 15$ and $b = 3$

Finally, f(a + b) = f(−2 + 3) = f(1)

f(1) = 5(1) − 2 = 3.

49) Answer: D

The ratio of $x : y$ is equivalent to x divided by y, or $\frac{x}{y}$.

Equation: $8x = 6y$

Dividing both sides by 8: $x = \frac{6y}{8}$

Dividing both sides by y: $\frac{x}{y} = \frac{6}{8} = \frac{3}{4}$

Then, $x : y$ is $3 : 4$

50) Answer: B

Method 1:

The formula for measurement of each angle of a regular polygon:

$x = \frac{180(n-2)}{n}$, (x is the measurement of the interior angle; n is the number of sides)

Substituting the given information:

$\frac{180(n-2)}{n} = 144 \rightarrow 180n - 360 = 144n \rightarrow 180n - 144\,n = 360$

$\rightarrow 36\,n = 360 \rightarrow n = 10$; The polygon has 10 angles and 10 sides.

Method 2:

The sum of exterior angles of any polygon is always equal to 360 degrees.

Exterior angle(degrees) $\times n = 360$; (n, is the number of angles (sides)).

Exterior angle = 180 − interior angle

The exterior angle = 180 − 144 = 36 degrees

Then, $36\,n = 360 \rightarrow n = 360 \div 36 = 10$

The polygon has 10 angles and 10 sides.

51) Answer: C

Age of Jim: x and the age of Jim 5 years ago: $x - 5$

The age of Frank: $4x$ and the age of Frank 5 years ago: $4x - 5$

$$(x - 5)(4x - 5) = 46$$

$$4x^2 - 5x - 20x + 25 = 46 \rightarrow 4x^2 - 25x - 21 = 0$$

$$(4x + 3)(x - 7) = 0$$

$4x + 3 = 0$ will yield a negative value for x, so this is not possible solution.

$x - 7 = 0 \rightarrow x = 7 \rightarrow$ The age of Frank: $4x = 4(7) = 28$.

52) Answer: B

$\frac{d}{4} = \frac{16}{d}$ Cross-multiply: $d \times d = 4 \times 4 \rightarrow d^2 = 64$

Then, find the square root of both sides:

The actual square root of d^2 is $\pm d$ and the actual square root of 64 is ± 8, so:

$$d = \pm 8$$

Of the answer choices for this question, -8 is the best choice since it is the only

one that is true about the equation.

53) Answer: A

Let f be the points earned by FT, r be the points scored by RT, and g be the points

scored by GT.

f $= 45\% \ of \ 160 = 0.45 \times 160 = 72$ points

$160 = f + r + g \rightarrow 160 = 72 + 3g + g \rightarrow 160 - 72 = 4g$

$\rightarrow 4g = 88 \rightarrow g = 22$; r $= 3g \rightarrow$ r $= 3(22) = 66$ points

54) Answer: A

If x is the smaller consecutive integer, then $x + 1$ is the larger consecutive

integer. Use their sum (-15) to find x:

$$x + (x + 1) = -15 \rightarrow 2x + 1 = -15 \rightarrow 2x = -16 \rightarrow x = -8$$

The two consecutive integers are -8 and -7.

One is added to the smaller integer: $-8 + 1 = -7$

and 2 is subtracted from the larger integer: $-7 - 2 = -9$

Find the product: $(-7)(-9) = 63$

55) Answer: B

The total number of handballs in the container is, $7 + 10 + 4 + 8 + 11 = 40$

Since there are 4 yellow handballs, the probability of selecting a green handball is

$$\frac{4}{40} = \frac{1}{10}$$

56) Answer: A

$3 + (5n + 8) - (6n + 5) = 3 + 5n + 8 - 6n - 5 = 6 - n$

57) Answer: C

Jimmy has 147 pages left to read $(161 - 14)$. $\frac{14}{20} = \frac{42}{60}$

He read at a rate of 42 pages per 1 hour. Then, divide the total number of pages

remaining (147) by the number of pages he can read per hour (42):

$$\frac{147}{42} = 3\frac{1}{2}$$

58) Answer: B

Two parallel lines (m & side BC) intersected by side AB,

$n = 65°$ (Interior angles)

59) Answer: D

Let x represent the number of pounds that can be bought for \$14.00.

$$\frac{1}{2.70} = \frac{x}{14}$$

Cross multiply and solve the equation: $2.70x = 14 \rightarrow x = \frac{14}{2.70} = 5.2$

60) Answer: B

Let x represent the distance you are trying to find (in km).

The quickest way to solve for x is to create a proportion with the quantities

you do know. $\frac{km\ on\ ground}{cm\ on\ map}$; Substitute the numbers you know: $\frac{9}{12} = \frac{x}{15}$

Cross-multiply to get this equation and solve: $9 \times 15 = 12x \rightarrow x = \frac{135}{12} = 11.25$

61) Answer: C

To write a percent, move the decimal point two places to the right and follow the resulting number with the % sign. Or adding the % sign after multiplying the decimal number and 100: $0.004 \times 100 = 0.4\% = 0.40\%$

62) Answer: A

$$\frac{(90 - x)}{7} = 2x \rightarrow 90 - x = 7(2x) \rightarrow 90 = 14x + x \rightarrow x = \frac{90}{15} = 6$$

63) Answer: C

Base salary: $54,000.

Health benefits: $54,000 \times 12\% = \$54,000 \times 0.12 = \$6,480$.

Her base salary, plus benefits: $54,000 + $6,480 = $60,480.

Since her total compensation: $63,000; Bonus: $63,000 – $60,480 = $2,520.

Calculate the percent of her bonus: $\frac{2,520}{60,480} = \frac{x}{100} \rightarrow x = \frac{252,000}{60,480} = 4.2$

64) Answer: B

Note: "@" and "#" are two "operations", and they are defined in the first two lines of the question.

Begin by evaluating $f(2)$ and $f(-1)$, Then, substitute $f(2)$ and $f(-1)$ into the first operation and substitute the appropriate values into the second operation.

$f(2) = -2(2)^2 + 3 = -8 + 3 = -5$

$f(-1) = -2(-1)^2 + 3 = -2 + 3 = 1$

$a @ b = a - 2ab$:

$(f(2) @ f(-1)) = (-5) @ (1) = (-5) - 2(1)(-5) = -5 + 10 = 5$

$a \# b = 2a - b^2$:

$f(2) \# (f(2) @ f(-1)) = (-5) \# 5 = 2(-5) - (5)^2 = -10 - 25 = -35$

"END"

Made in the USA
Middletown, DE
29 October 2023

41574371R00119